G000292426

Answer Book

Introduction

Pupils' written work

Abacus Evolve textbooks provide clear guidance to pupils on how their work should be recorded. Pupils should be encouraged to follow this guidance, which will make marking their work substantially easier and clearly focused.

Marking pupils' work

Clearly it is important that pupils' work is seen and checked by the teacher regularly, but it is not necessary for all work to be marked by the teacher. Decisions about which work should be teacher-marked, and how it should be marked will be made alongside the need to maximise time available for teaching and guiding pupils through their activities.

A suggested approach within *Abacus Evolve* is to make these decisions Block by Block. Decide, for example, for each Block, which parts you want to mark, and which parts the pupils can mark.

Marking the 'Owls'

The 'Owls' are optional problem-solving or investigational activities for extra challenge on each page. They should generally be marked by the teacher. The pupils' responses to the 'Owls' may well vary because of the often open-ended nature of the activities, however the answers give suggestions where appropriate. Pupils should also be encouraged to use a systematic approach to solving these problems, where relevant.

For many 'Owls' you may want to ask the pupils to work in groups or pairs, possibly leading to a group display of their results.

Contents

Block AI

Page 3
Multiplying by 10 and 100

1. H T U
   3 6 1 × 100 = 36 100
   Value = 30 thousand
2. H T U
   4 5 2 × 100 = 45 200
   Value = 5 thousand
3. T U
   6 8 × 100 = 6 800
   Value = 8 hundred
4. H T U
   7 1 6 × 100 = 71 600
   Value = 1 thousand
5. H T U
   6 0 5 × 100 = 60 500
   Value = 60 thousand
6. H T U
   4 2 4 × 100 = 42 400
   Value = 40 thousand
7. H T U
   2 8 1 × 100 = 28 100
   Value = 1 hundred
8. H T U
   3 4 8 × 100 = 34 800
   Value = 30 thousand
9. H T U
   9 9 9 × 100 = 99 900
   Value = 9 thousand
10. H T U
    1 1 0 × 100 = 11 000
    Value = 1 thousand
11. H T U
    1 9 3 × 100 = 19 300
    Value = 9 thousand
12. T U
    9 1 × 100 = 9 100
    Value = 1 hundred
13. H T U
    7 6 3 × 100 = 76 300
    Value = 6 thousand
14. d
15. a
16. b
17. c
18. a
19. b
Owl 6

Page 4
Multiplying by 10, 100 and 1000

1. a and m
   b and c
   f and j
   g and o
   k and x
   l and t
   p and i
   q and r
   u and e
   v and w
2. 1200 months in a century
   12 000 months in a millennium
   5200 weeks in a century
   52 000 weeks in a millennium
3. £47
   £470
4. £1500
   £1560
5. 273 × 100 = 27 300
6. 3648 × 10 = 36 480
7. 4875 × 10 = 48 750
8. 314 × 1000 = 314 000
9. 402 × 1000 = 402 000
10. 7679 × 1000 = 7 679 000
11. 5138 × 100 = 513 800
12. 620 × 10 = 6200
13. 532 × 100 = 53 200
Owl Answers may vary. It should take
    the person multiplying by 10 six
    times to reach over a million, and
    the person multiplying by 100 three
    times. However, how many times it
    takes you to reach over *six* million
    depends upon your start number.

Page 5

Multiplying by 10, 100 and 1000

1. £5·50 × 10 = £55
2. £3·40 × 10 = £34
3. £10·50 × 10 = £105
4. £6·65 × 10 = £66·50
5. £4·44 × 10 = £44·40
6. £7·75 × 10 = £77·50
7. £3·29 × 10 = £32·90
8. £6·25 × 10 = £62·50
9. £5·46 × 10 = £54·60
10. £10·33 × 10 = £103·30
11. £8·66 × 10 = £86·60

Wages for doing each job 100 times:

1. £5·50 × 100 = £550
2. £3·40 × 100 = £340
3. £10·50 × 100 = £1050
4. £6·65 × 100 = £665
5. £4·44 × 100 = £444
6. £7·75 × 100 = £775
7. £3·29 × 100 = £329
8. £6·25 × 100 = £625
9. £5·46 × 100 = £546
10. £10·33 × 100 = £1033
11. £8·66 × 100 = £866
12. true
13. false
14. false
15. true
16. false

Owl Multiplying £5·50 by 10 five times = £550 000. Less than £1 000 000

Page 6

Multiplying by 10, 100 and 1000

1. 3·64 × 100 = 364 cm
2. 4·8 × 100 = 480 cm
3. 2·08 × 100 = 208 cm
4. 14·07 × 100 = 1407 cm
5. 0·86 × 100 = 86 cm
6. 0·24 × 100 = 24 cm
7. 13·06 × 1000 = 13 060

8. 20·08 × 100 = 2008
9. 203·4 × 100 = 20 340
10. 345·04 × 1000 = 345 040
11. 100 × 20·08 = 2008
12. 14·05 × 1000 = 14 050
13. 10 × 195·3 = 1953
14. 38·06 × 1000 = 38 060

Explore 9 amounts between £1 and £2;
89 amounts between £1 and £10

Page 7

Dividing by 10 and 100

1. a and k
   b and l
   c and n
   d and q
   e and j
   f and i
2. 3500 ÷ 100 = 35 m
3. 400 ÷ 100 = 4 m
4. 5100 ÷ 100 = 51 m
5. 6200 ÷ 100 = 62 m
6. 21 000 ÷ 100 = 210 m
7. 6700 ÷ 100 = 67 m
8. 48 000 ÷ 100 = 480 m
9. 900 ÷ 100 = 9 m
10. 7600 ÷ 100 = 76 m
11. 59 000 ÷ 100 = 590 m
12. 800 ÷ 100 = 8 m
13. 3900 ÷ 100 = 39 m

Owl 200; you could also have slices of 20 g, 40 g, 50 g, 100 g, 200 g, 400 g, 500 g and 1000 g

Page 8

Dividing by 10, 100 and 1000

1. c
2. a
3. d
4. d
5. a

6. d
7. c
8. b
9. false
10. true
11. true
12. 16 litres
13. 15 litres
14. 31 litres
15. 114 litres
16. 1 litre
17. 45 litres
18. 2 litres
19. 105 litres
Owl 8

Page 9

Dividing by 10, 100 and 1000

1. $507 \div 100 = £5·07$
2. $643 \div 100 = £6·43$
3. $777 \div 100 = £7·77$
4. $1004 \div 100 = £10·04$
5. $990 \div 100 = £9·90$
6. $7040 \div 100 = £70·40$
7. $101 \div 100 = £1·01$
8. $2301 \div 100 = £23·01$
9. $648 \div 100 = £6·48$
10. $3709 \div 100 = £37·09$
11. $876 \div 100 = £8·76$
12. $2500 \div 100 = £25·00$
13. $1400 m \div 1000 = 1·4 km$
14. $4780 m \div 1000 = 4·78 km$
15. $3660 ml \div 1000 = 3·66 l$
16. $700 ml \div 1000 = 0·7 l$
17. $4880 g \div 1000 = 4·88 kg$
18. $5700 m \div 1000 = 5·7 km$
19. $6990 ml \div 1000 = 6·99 l$
20. $4820 g \div 1000 = 4·82 kg$
21. $3650 m \div 1000 = 3·65 km$
Owl Answers may vary.
Explore 9 (if you don't include the
amounts of $100 or $1000)

Page 10

Dividing by 10, 100 and 1000

1. $4260 \div 100 = 42·6$
   42 100 g weights
   6 10 g weights
2. $33790 \div 100 = 337·9$
   337 100 g weights
   9 10 g weights
3. $5470 \div 100 = 54·7$
   54 100 g weights
   7 10 g weights
4. $2180 \div 100 = 21·8$
   21 100 g weights
   8 10 g weights
5. $6190 \div 100 = 61·9$
   61 100 g weights
   9 10 g weights
6. $48210 \div 100 = 482·1$
   482 100 g weights
   1 10 g weight
7. $3940 \div 100 = 39·4$
   39 100 g weights
   4 10 g weights
8. $12590 \div 100 = 125·9$
   125 100 g weights
   9 10 g weights
9. $3010 \div 1000 = 3·01$
10. $41·36 \div 1000 = 0·04136$
11. $38·94 \div 10 = 3·894$
12. $3·6 \div 100 = 0·036$
13. $90·9 \div 1000 = 0·0909$
14. $3·6 \div 100 = 0·036$
15. $0·2 \div 10 = 0·02$
16. $63·4 \div 10 = 6·34$
17. £10·40; £20·80
18. $1·345 m$
19. 2046 notes; 204·6 bundles

Page 11

Multiplying and dividing

1. a) 18   b) 36   c) 48
2. d) 16   e) 56   f) 72
3. g) 28   h) 42   i) 56

4. $4 \times 7 = 28$
5. $8 \times 6 = 48$
6. $35 \div 5 = 7$
7. $9 \times 3 = 27$
8. $63 \div 9 = 7$
9. $8 \times 8 = 64$
10. $42 \div 6 = 7$
11. $32 \div 4 = 8$
12. $7 \times 8 = 56$
13. $9 \times 4 = 36$
14. $40 \div 5 = 8$
15. $24 \div 3 = 8$
16. $6 \times 8 = 48$
17. $49 \div 7 = 7$
18. $9 \times 8 = 72$
19. $24 \div 6 = 4$
20. 13
21. 31
22. 17
23. 15

Owl Answers may vary.

Page 12
Multiplying and dividing

1.
×	4	7	3	5
2	8	14	6	10
8	32	56	24	40
6	24	42	18	30
9	36	63	27	45

2.
×	9	7	8	5
8	72	56	64	40
4	36	28	32	20
9	81	63	72	45
6	54	42	48	30

3.
×	60	80	50	70
3	180	240	150	210
2	120	160	100	140
4	240	320	200	280
6	360	480	300	420

4.
×	7	8	9	6
20	140	160	180	120
40	280	320	360	240
30	210	240	270	180
50	350	400	450	300

5. $24 \div 8 = 3$
6. $7 \times 7 = 49$
7. $8 \times 9 = 72$
8. $32 \div 4 = 8$
9. $42 \div 6 = 7$
10. $4 \times 8 = 32$

Explore Answers may vary.

Page 13
Multiplying and dividing

1. 2 weeks
2. 164 kg
3. £119
4. 16
5. $7 \times 6 = 42$
6. $45 \div 9 = 5$
7. $36 \div 6 = 6$
8. $7 \times 8 = 56$
9. $72 \div 9 = 8$
10. $5 \times 9 = 45$
11. $32 \div 4 = 8$
12. $21 \div 3 = 7$

Explore

1	2	3	4	5	6	7	8
2	4	6	8	10	12	14	16
3	6	9	12	15	18	21	24
4	8	12	16	20	24	28	32
5	10	15	20	25	30	35	40
6	12	18	24	30	36	42	48
7	14	21	28	35	42	49	56
8	16	24	32	40	48	56	64

1	2	3	4	5	6	7	8
2	4	6	8	1	3	5	7
3	6	9	3	6	9	3	6
4	8	3	7	2	6	1	5
5	1	6	2	7	3	8	4
6	3	9	6	3	9	6	3
7	5	3	1	8	6	4	2
8	7	6	5	4	3	2	1

Page 14

Multiplying and dividing

1. First code = ×8 table: a = 4, b = 7,
   c = 2, d = 9, e = 6, f = 8, g = 1,
   h = 5, i = 0, j = 3
   Second code = ×7 table: a = 3,
   b = 5, c = 1, d = 4, e = 2, f = 6,
   g = 7, h = 9, i = 8
   Third code = ×7 table: k = 3, l = 5,
   m = 1, n = 4, o = 2, p = 6, q = 7,
   r = 9, s = 8
2. 80
3. 25
4. 50
5. 3
6. 4
7. 40
8. 6
9. 9
10. 11

Owl Answers may vary.

Page 15

Remainders

1. $5\frac{1}{2}$
2. $8\frac{1}{4}$
3. $8\frac{2}{5}$
4. $7\frac{2}{3}$

5. $3\frac{1}{6}$
6. $4\frac{3}{7}$
7. $4\frac{7}{10}$
8. $3\frac{2}{9}$
9. $6\frac{2}{8}$ (or $\frac{1}{4}$)
10. $6\frac{3}{4}$
11. $7\frac{3}{6}$ (or $\frac{1}{2}$)
12. $9\frac{4}{9}$
13. $43 \div 2 = 21\frac{1}{2}$
14. $43 \div 3 = 14\frac{1}{3}$
15. $43 \div 4 = 10\frac{3}{4}$
16. $43 \div 5 = 8\frac{3}{5}$
17. $43 \div 6 = 7\frac{1}{6}$
18. $43 \div 7 = 6\frac{1}{7}$
19. $43 \div 8 = 5\frac{3}{8}$
20. $43 \div 9 = 4\frac{7}{9}$
21. $43 \div 10 = 4\frac{3}{10}$

For 67 macaroons:

13. $67 \div 2 = 33\frac{1}{2}$
14. $67 \div 3 = 22\frac{1}{3}$
15. $67 \div 4 = 16\frac{3}{4}$
16. $67 \div 5 = 13\frac{2}{5}$
17. $67 \div 6 = 11\frac{1}{6}$
18. $67 \div 7 = 9\frac{4}{7}$
19. $67 \div 8 = 8\frac{3}{8}$
20. $67 \div 9 = 7\frac{4}{9}$
21. $67 \div 10 = 6\frac{7}{10}$

Owl Answers may vary.

Page 16

Remainders

1. $14\frac{1}{3}$ teams
2. $5\frac{5}{7}$ teams
3. $10\frac{2}{5}$ teams
4. $7\frac{4}{6}$ (or $\frac{2}{3}$) teams
5. $6\frac{1}{5}$ teams
6. $7\frac{7}{10}$ teams
7. $9\frac{4}{9}$ teams

8. $7\frac{5}{8}$ teams

9. $8\frac{1}{6}$ teams

10. $3\frac{2}{3} = 11 \div 3$

11. $4\frac{1}{4} = 17 \div 4$

12. $5\frac{3}{5} = 28 \div 5$

13. $6\frac{4}{7} = 46 \div 7$

14. $7\frac{3}{8} = 59 \div 8$

15. $2\frac{1}{6} = 13 \div 6$

16. $3\frac{7}{10} = 37 \div 10$

17. $1\frac{4}{9} = 13 \div 9$

18. $3\frac{7}{8} = 31 \div 8$

19. $4\frac{7}{12} = 55 \div 12$

20. $3\frac{6}{11} = 39 \div 11$

21. $2\frac{13}{20} = 53 \div 20$

Owl Answers may vary.

Page 17
Remainders

1. $32 \div 10 = 3\cdot2$
2. $43 \div 10 = 4\cdot3$
3. $19 \div 10 = 1\cdot9$
4. $27 \div 10 = 2\cdot7$
5. $58 \div 10 = 5\cdot8$
6. $64 \div 10 = 6\cdot4$
7. $130 \div 10 = 13$
8. $202 \div 10 = 20\cdot2$
9. $136 \div 100 = 1\cdot36$
10. $214 \div 100 = 2\cdot14$
11. $326 \div 100 = 3\cdot26$
12. $178 \div 100 = 1\cdot78$
13. $291 \div 100 = 2\cdot91$
14. $432 \div 100 = 4\cdot32$
15. $906 \div 100 = 9\cdot06$
16. $1008 \div 100 = 10\cdot08$

17. A: 4·16, B: 4·2, E: 4·25, D: 4·5, C: 4·8

18. C: 3·4, D: 3·5, A: 3·61, B: 3·7, E: 3·75

19. C: 8·2, E: 8·25, A: 8·27, B: 8·3, D: 8·5

Owl Answers may vary. If he eats 13 biscuits a day in March, he eats 403 biscuits in total, which = 4·03 bags. Estimates should be 3·9 to 4 bags (30 × 13 = 390, rounded to 400). Estimates for February should be between 3·6 and 3·9.

Page 18
Remainders

1. $\frac{41}{10} = 4\cdot1$
2. $5\cdot8 \div 2 = 2\cdot9$
3. $\frac{33}{5} = 6\cdot6$
4. $37 \div 10 = 3\cdot7$
5. $8\cdot5 \div 5 = 1\cdot7$
6. $\frac{15}{4} = 3\cdot75$
7. $9 \div 4 = 2\cdot25$
8. $\frac{62}{10} = 6\cdot2$
9. $\frac{18}{4} = 4\cdot5$
10. $39 \div 2 = 19\cdot5$
11. $\frac{27}{5} = 5\cdot4$
12. $36 \div 5 = 7\cdot2$
13. 1·3 and 1·4
14. 3·2 and 3·3
15. 5·3 and 5·5
16. 8·2 and 8·4
17. 5·8 and 5·9
18. 2·6 and 2·7
19. 1·2 and 1·3
20. 1·6 and 1·7

Explore Answers may vary.

Block BI

Page 19

Odd and even

1.

1	2	3	4	5	6	7	8	9	10
2	4	6	8	10	12	14	16	18	20
3	6	9	12	15	18	21	24	27	30
4	8	12	16	20	24	28	32	36	40
5	10	15	20	25	30	35	40	45	50
6	12	18	24	30	36	42	48	54	60
7	14	21	27	35	42	49	56	63	70
8	16	24	32	40	48	56	64	72	80
9	18	27	36	45	54	63	72	81	90
10	20	30	40	50	60	70	80	90	100

The coloured numbers are all odd.
The remaining numbers are all even.

2.

×	O	E
O	O	E
E	E	E

Children's examples in the following questions may vary:

3. 3 × odd = odd
4. odd/even × 4 = even
5. 3 × 2 × odd/even = even
6. odd × odd = odd
7. odd/even × even = even
8. even × 3 = even

Page 20

Odd and even

1. even
2. even
3. even
4. even
5. even
6. odd
7. even
8. odd
9. odd
10. even
11. even
12. even
13. odd
14. even
15. even
16. odd
17. even
18. odd
19. even
20. odd
21. even
Owl Answers may vary. Has to end in ·5, e.g. 3·5
Explore Answers may vary.

Page 21

Odd and even

1. odd
2. even
3. even
4. even
5. even
6. even
7. even
8. even
9. odd
10. even
11. odd
12. even
13. even
14. odd
15. even/odd
16. even
17. even
18. even
19. true
20. true
21. true
22. true

23. true
24. false
Owl Answers may vary. They could be any combination of odd and even, as long as one of them is even.

Page 22
Cubic numbers

1st Explore Answers may vary. Cubic numbers up to 10^3 are: 1, 8, 27, 64, 125, 216, 343, 512, 729, 1000. The pattern goes odd, even, odd, even, odd, even…

2nd Explore Answers may vary. The rows all total to give cubic numbers: first row is 1^3, second row is 2^3, third row is 3^3, etc.

Page 23
Common multiples

1. 7, 14, 21, 28, 35, 42, 49, 56, 63, 70
2. 4, 8, 12, 16, 20, 24, 28, 32, 36, 40, 48, 56, 60, 64, 72, 80, 100
3. 9, 18, 27, 36, 45, 54, 63, 72, 81, 90
4. 6, 12, 18, 24, 30, 36, 42, 48, 54, 60, 72, 90
5. 12, 24, 36, 48, 60, 72
6. 14, 28, 42, 56, 70
7. 12, 24, 36, 48, 60, 72
8. 8, 16, 24, 32, 40, 48, 56, 64, 72, 80
9. 20, 40, 60, 80, 100
10. 6
11. 10
12. 12
13. 15
14. 4
15. 12
16. 12
17. 24
18. 24
19. 40
20. 30

21. 150
Explore Answers may vary. Possible answers include: 60: a common multiple of 3, 4 and 5, and 4, 5 and 6; 6: a common multiple of 1, 2 and 3; 210: common multiple of 5, 6 and 7.

Page 24
Common multiples

1. 8, 32, 60, 40, 16, 24, 20, 48, 36
2. 21, 42, 60, 24, 48, 18, 36
3. 42, 60, 24, 48,18, 36
4. 60, 24, 48, 36
5. 60, 40, 20
6. 42, 14
7. 21, 42
8. 40
9. 60, 24, 48, 36
10. 60

Answers to the second part to questions 1–10 may vary.

11.

	2	3	4
5	10	15	20
6	12	18	24
7	14	21	28

12.

	2	8	5
3	6	24	15
9	18	72	45
4	8	32	20

13.

	10	4	6
5	50	20	30
20	200	80	120
2	20	8	12

14.

	15	10	2
3	45	30	6
9	135	90	18
4	60	40	8

Owl Answers may vary. Possible answers include: 1, 5, 7, 11, 13, 17, 19, 23, 25, 29, 31, 37, 41, 47, 53...

Page 25
Common multiples

Answers to questions 1–12 may vary.
1. 14, 28, 42
2. 12, 24, 36
3. 15, 30, 45
4. 30, 60, 90
5. 20, 40, 60
6. 15, 30, 45
7. 100, 200, 300
8. 36, 72, 108
9. 40, 80, 120
10. 30, 60, 90
11. 60, 120, 180
12. 150, 300, 450

Smallest common multiple in each set:
1. 14
2. 12
3. 15
4. 30
5. 20
6. 15
7. 100
8. 36
9. 40
10. 30
11. 60
12. 150

Explore

×	2	3	4	5	6	7	8	9
2	2	6	4	10	6	14	8	18
3	6	3	12	15	6	21	24	9
4	4	12	4	20	12	28	8	36
5	10	15	20	5	30	35	40	45
6	6	6	12	30	6	42	24	18
7	14	21	28	35	42	7	56	63
8	8	24	8	40	24	56	8	72
9	18	9	36	45	18	63	72	9

Page 26
Common multiples

1. 84
2. 18
3. 48
4. 180
5. 24
6. 36

Owl $\frac{1}{4}$ and $\frac{1}{3}$

Explore
a) $\frac{7}{6}$
b) $\frac{31}{20}$
c) $\frac{17}{12}$
d) $\frac{13}{10}$
e) $\frac{23}{24}$
f) $\frac{8}{9}$
g) $\frac{17}{12}$
h) $\frac{18}{10}$
i) $\frac{49}{24}$

Page 27
Parallelograms

1.

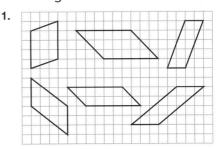

2. a = 102° b = 78° c = 102° d = 78°
3. a = 114° b = 66° c = 114° d = 66°

Owl Answers may vary.

Page 28
Quadrilaterals

1. parallelogram
2. rectangle
3. rhombus
4. trapezium
5. trapezium

6. rectangle
7. trapezium
8. trapezium
9. parallelogram
10. parallelogram
11. parallelogram
12. parallelogram

Number of pairs of parallel sides in each shape:
1. 2
2. 2
3. 2
4. 1
5. 1
6. 2
7. 1
8. 1
9. 2
10. 2
11. 2
12. 2
Explore Answers may vary.

Page 29
Quadrilaterals

1. true
2. true
3. true
4. true
5. true
6. false
7. true
8. true
9. false
10. false
11. true
12. true
1st Explore Answers may vary.
2nd Explore Answers may vary.

Page 30
Quadrilaterals

1. squares, rectangles, parallelograms, rhombuses, trapeziums

2. squares, rectangles, parallelograms, rhombuses
3. squares, rhombuses
4. any other quadrilaterals
Explore Answers may vary.

Page 31
Kites and arrowheads

1.

2.

3.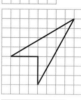

4.

5.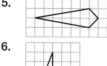

6.

7.

8.

Owl Answers may vary.

Explore Answers may vary.
Angles always cross at 90°.

Page 32
Quadrilaterals

1. arrowhead
2. rhombus
3. arrowhead
4. rhombus
5. kite
6. trapezium
7. kite
8. parallelogram
9. trapezium

Angles:
1. three acute, one reflex
2. two acute, two obtuse
3. three acute, one reflex
4. two acute, two obtuse
5. one acute, 3 obtuse
6. two acute, two obtuse
7. one acute, 3 obtuse
8. two acute, two obtuse
9. two acute, two obtuse
10. true
11. true
12. true
13. true
14. false
15. false
16. false
17. true
18. true

Owl Answers may vary.

Page 33
Quadrilaterals

1.

	square	rectangle	parallelogram	rhombus	trapezium	kite	arrowhead
Has 4 sides	red	red	red	red	red	red	red
Has all sides the same length	red	green	green	red	green	green	green
Has one pair of opposite sides parallel	green	green	green	green	red	green	green
Has two pairs of opposite sides parallel	red	red	red	red	green	green	green
Has opposite sides equal	red	red	red	red	yellow	green	green
Has adjacent sides equal	red	green	green	red	yellow	red	red
Has line symmetry	red	red	green	red	yellow	red	red
Has a right angle	red	red	green	green	yellow	yellow	yellow
Has an obtuse angle	green	green	red	red	red	red	yellow
Has a reflex angle	green	green	green	green	green	green	red

NB: it is assumed that children will understand 'rectangle' as all rectangles except squares, and 'parallelogram' as all parallelograms except rhombuses.

Explore Answers may vary.

Block C1

Page 34

Pictograms

1. 23 songs
2. 4 songs
3. 31 songs
4. 18 songs
5. 3 min–3 min 59s
6. 0–59s
7. 4 min–4 min 59s and 0–59s
8. 1 min–1 min 59s, 2 min–2 min 59, 3 min–3 min 59s
9. 3 min–3 min 59s

Owl Answers may vary.

Page 35

Pictograms

1. 15 programmes
2. 9 programmes
3. 12 programmes
4. 68 programmes
5. 26 programmes
6. 47 programmes
7. 11–20 minutes
8. 51–60 minutes
9. 3 programme lengths: 0–10, 11–20 and 21–30 minutes
10. 4 programme lengths: 0–10, 11–20, 21–30 and 31–40 minutes
11. 2 programme lengths: 41–50 and 51–60 minutes
12. 11–20 minutes
13. 80

Owl Answers may vary.

Page 36

Pictograms

1. 41–60
2. 2–20
3. 41–60
4. 22

5. 27
6. 23
7. 10
8. 4
9. 10
10. 2–20
11. 61–80
12. 21–40
13. 2–20, 21–40 or 61–80
14. 41–60 or 81–100
15. Answers will vary.
16. Answers will vary.

Page 37

Pictograms

1.-9. Answers will vary.

Owl Answers will vary.

Page 38

Grouping data

1. By the number of packets eaten per month.
2. 11–15
3. 22
4. 4
5. 88
6. 1–30
7. 35
8. 12
9. 63

Owl Answers may vary.

Page 39

Grouping data

1. Yes

2.

Minutes watched	30–60	61–90	91–120	121–150	151–180	181–210
Number of people	5	12	10	11	7	5

3.

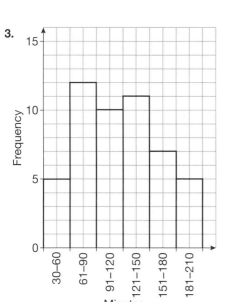

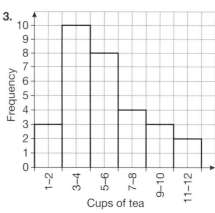

4. 3–4
5. 11–12
6. a) 9   b) 3   c) 22
7. false
8. 1–2 per day ⟶ 7–14 per week
3–4 per day ⟶ 21–28 per week
5–6 per day ⟶ 35–42 per week
7–8 per day ⟶ 49–56 per week
9–10 per day ⟶ 63–70 per week
11–12 per day ⟶ 77–84 per week
Owl Answers may vary.

4. 30 minutes to 210 minutes (or half an hour to three and a half hours)
5. 61–90 minutes
6. 12
7. 17
8. 21
9. 5
Owl Answers may vary.

Page 40
Grouping data

1.

Cups	1–2	3–4	5–6	7–8	9–10	11–12
Tallies	|||	ЖЖ	Ж |||	||||	|||	||

2.

Cups	1–2	3–4	5–6	7–8	9–10	11–12
Frequency	3	10	8	4	3	2

Page 41
Metres, centimetres and millimetres

1. 0·36 m = 36 cm
36 cm = 360 mm
2. 0·48 m = 48 cm
48 cm = 480 mm
3. 0·66 m = 66 cm
66 cm = 660 mm
4. 0·74 m = 74 cm
74 cm = 740 mm
5. 1·26 m = 126 cm
126 cm = 1260 mm
6. 1·07 m = 107 cm
107 cm = 1070 mm
7. 1·69 m = 169 cm
169 cm = 1690 mm

8. 1·33 m = 133 cm
    133 cm = 1330 mm
9. 1·04 m = 104 cm
    104 cm = 1040 mm
10. 10 × 100 m = 1 km
    10 pipes
11. 5 × 200 m = 1 km
    5 pipes
12. 20 × 50 m = 1 km
    20 pipes
13. 8 × 125 m = 1 km
    8 pipes
14. 4 × 250 m = 1 km
    4 pipes
15. 40 × 25 m = 1 km
    40 pipes
16. 2 × 500 m = 1 km
    2 pipes
17. 16 × 62·5 m = 1 km
    16 pipes
Owl Answers may vary.

Page 42
Metres, centimetres and millimetres

1. 0·38 m × 0·334 m
    380 mm × 334 mm
2. 0·4 m × 0·161 m
    400 mm × 161 mm
3. 0·42 m × 0·216 m
    420 mm × 216 mm
4. 0·327 m × 0·180 m
    327 mm × 180 mm
5. 0·41 m × 0·093 m
    410 mm × 93 mm
6. 0·35 m × 0·362 m
    350 mm × 362 mm
7. 0·44 m × 0·403 m
    440 mm × 403 mm
8. 0·37 m × 0·294 m
    370 mm × 294 mm

9. 0·46 m × 0·429 m
    460 mm × 429 mm
10. 0·276 m × 0·29 m
    276 mm × 290 mm
11. 0·36 m × 0·434 m
    360 mm × 434 mm
12. 0·31 m × 0·243 m
    310 mm × 243 mm
13. 4 cm = 40 mm
    40 ÷ 100 = 0·4 mm
14. 7 cm = 70 mm
    70 ÷ 100 = 0·7 mm
15. 2 cm = 20 mm
    20 ÷ 100 = 0·2 mm
16. 5·4 cm = 54 mm
    54 ÷ 100 = 0·54 mm
17. 3·2 cm = 32 mm
    32 ÷ 100 = 0·32 mm
18. 6·1 cm = 61 mm
    61 ÷ 100 = 0·61 mm
Owl Answers may vary.

Page 43
Kilometres, metres, centimetres and millimetres

1. 4 children
2. 14 children
3. 10 children
4. 24 children
5. 17 children
6. 50 children
7. 7 children
8. 19 children
9. 4 children
10. 1·3 cm = 13 mm
11. 101 m = 0·101 km
12. 0·4 mm = 0·04 cm
13. 2·4 m = 0·0024 km
14. 0·03 m = 30 mm
15. 6202 mm = 6·202 m
16. 5·005 m = 500·5 cm
17. 1·07 cm = 10·7 mm
Owl Answers may vary.

Page 44
Metres and miles

1. 4000 m = 4 km
   4 km = 2·5 miles
2. 2000 m = 2 km
   2 km = 1·25 miles
3. 1000 m = 1 km
   1 km = 0·625 miles
4. 1600 m = 1·6 km
   1·6 km = 1 mile
5. 400 m = 0·4 km
   0·4 km = 0·25 miles
6. 3200 m = 3·2 km
   3·2 km = 2 miles
7. 4800 m = 4·8 km
   4·8 km = 3 miles
8. 200 m = 0·2 km
   0·2 km = 0·125 miles
9. 10 000 m = 10 km
   10 km = 6·25 miles
10. 0·85 m; 0·17 mm
11. 0·464 m
12. 8·2 mm; 48

Explore Answers may vary.

Page 45
Kilograms and grams

1. 942 g = 0·942 kg
2. 705 g = 0·705 kg
3. 1704 g = 1·704 kg
4. 1900 g = 1·9 kg
5. 812 g = 0·812 kg
6. 1010 g = 1·01 kg
7. 1235 g = 1·235 kg
8. 46 g = 0·046 kg
9. 70 g = 0·07 kg
10. 4 kg; 4·5 kg
11. 2·6 kg
12. 1·05 kg

Owl Answers may vary.

Page 46
Tonnes, kilograms and grams

1. 2030 g
2. 3104 g
3. 1002 g
4. 4050 g
5. 6009 g
6. 850 g
7. 4270 g
8. 120 g
9. 1770 g
10. 45 kg = 0·045 tonnes
11. 56 kg = 0·056 tonnes
12. 4·6 tonnes = 4600 kg
13. 100 g = 0·1 kg
14. 530 g = 0·53 kg
15. 7367 g = 7·367 kg
16. 54 600 kg = 54·6 tonnes
17. 10 tonnes = 10 000 000 g

Owl Answers may vary.

Page 47
Kilograms, grams, pounds and ounces

1. 2·2 lb = 1 kg
2. 6·6 lb = 3 kg
3. 4·4 lb = 2 kg
4. 8·8 lb = 4 kg
5. 2 oz = 60 g
6. 5 oz = 150 g
7. 8 oz = 240 g
8. 3 oz = 90 g
9. 4 oz = 120 g
10. 7 oz = 210 g
11. 10 oz = 300 g
12. 6 oz = 180 g
13. 24 oz = $1\frac{1}{2}$ lb
14. 32 oz = 2 lb
15. $1\frac{1}{4}$ lb = 20 oz
16. 48 oz = 3 lb
17. 2·5 lb = 40 oz
18. 20 oz = 1·25 lb (or $1\frac{1}{4}$ lb)

19. 480 oz = 30 lb
20. 1·75 lb = 28 oz
21. $3\frac{3}{4}$ lb = 60 oz
22. 64 oz = 4 lb
Owl Yes

Page 48
Problems

1. false
2. true
3. true
4. true
5. true
6. true
7. true

Explore Two hundred and twenty 10 lb
weights make up 1 tonne.
About 157 stone make up
1 tonne. There are about 20
hundredweight in 1 tonne.

Block DI
Page 49
Angles

Estimates may vary.
1. estimate: 45°
measure: 46°
2. estimate: 20°
measure: 20°
3. estimate: 120°
measure: 120°
4. estimate: 90°
measure: 90°
5. estimate: 60°
measure: 60°
6. estimate: 30°
measure: 35°
7.

8.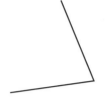

9.

10.

11.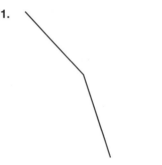

12.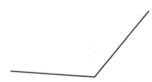

Owl Answers may vary.

Page 50
Angles at a point

1. a) 135°
b) 225°
Total 360°

2. a) 90°
b) 270°
Total 360°

3. a) 315°
b) 45°
Total 360°
4. a) 180°
b) 180°
Total 360°
5. a) 270°
b) 90°
Total 360°
6. a) 135°
b) 225°
Total 360°
7. 240°
8. 50°
9. 205°
10. 15°
11. 95°
12. 288°
13. 177°
14. 113°
15. a = 111°, b = 123°, c = 71°, d = 55°
16. a = 55°, b = 126°, c = 92°, d = 87°
Owl A = 60°, B = 120°, C = 180°

Page 51
Angles at a point

1. 140° + 170° = 310°
360° − 310° = 50°
2. 150° + 125° + 65° = 340°
360° − 340° = 20°
3. 100° + 85° + 75° = 260°
360° − 260° = 100°
4. 135° + 62° + 58° = 255°
360° − 255° = 105°
5. 110° + 75° + 85° = 270°
360° − 270° = 90°
6. 79° + 86° + 64° = 229°
360° − 229° = 131°
7. 85° + 75° + 65° + 55° = 280°
360° − 280° = 80°
8. 111° + 68° + 47° + 38° = 264°
360° − 264° = 96°

9. 125° + 85° + 15° + 65° = 290°
360° − 290° = 70°
10. 55°, 125° and 125°
11. 38°, 142° and 142°
Owl Answers may vary. All the angles should add up to 360°.

Page 52
Angles at a point

1. 45°
2. 150°
3. 60°
4. 75°
5. 120°
6. 135°
7. 90°
8. 180°
9. 30°
10. 75°
11. 15°
12. 165°
Larger angle:
1. 315°
2. 210°
3. 300°
4. 285°
5. 240°
6. 225°
7. 270°
8. 180°
9. 330°
10. 285°
11. 345°
12. 195°
Owl 2:30 or 9:30

Page 53
Angles in a triangle

1. a = 40°, b = 70°, c = 70°
2. a = 45°, b = 90°, c = 45°
3. a = 60°, b = 60°, c = 60°

4. a = 22·5°, b = 135°, c = 22·5°
They all add up to 180°.
Explore Answers may vary. Children
should notice that the angles
total 360°.

Page 54
Angles in a triangle

1. 55°
2. 28°
3. 15°
4. 62°
5. 31°
6. 57°
7. 132°
8. 144°
9. 34°

Explore 10° and 130°, 20° and 120°,
30° and 100°... 70° and 70°.
Two of these triangles could be
isosceles: the 40°, 40° and 90°
triangle, and the 40°, 70° and
70° triangle. If one of the angles
is 60°, and the other two are
both multiples of 10°, there are
no possible isosceles triangles,
only an equilateral triangle with
angles: 60°, 60° and 60°.

Page 55
Angles in a triangle

1. 80°
2. 34°
3. 104°
4. 109°
5. 102°
6. 123°
7. a = 71°, b = 71°
8. a = 54°, b = 54°, c = 72°
9. a = 46°, b = 46°, c = 88°
10. 66° and 66° or 48° and 84°

11. 81° and 81° or 18° and 144°
12. 57° and 57° or 66° and 48°
13. 48·5° and 48·5° or 66° and 48°
Owl An equilateral triangle has 3 angles
each of 60°, which is a multiple of 4,
5 and 6.

Page 56
Angles in a triangle

1. true
2. false
3. true
4. true
5. true
6. true
7. 73°
8. a =141° and b = 38°

Explore

Number of sides	Total of angles
4	Four right angles (360°)
5	Six right angles (540°)
6	Eight right angles (720°)
7	Ten right angles (900°)
8	Twelve right angles (1080°]

Page 57
Adding three and four numbers

1. £2 + £8 + £5 + £4 = £19
£1 change
2. £3 + £7 + £8 = £18
£2 change
3. £3 + £4 + £9 = £16
£4 change
4. £2 + £7 + £5 + £4 = £18
£2 change
5. 200 + 500 + 800 + 600 = 2100
6. 500 + 700 + 800 = 2000
7. 300 + 900 + 600 + 700 = 2500
8. 400 + 300 + 800 = 1500

9. $800 + 300 + 500 + 100 = 1700$
10. $600 + 400 + 300 + 500 = 1800$
Owl £1

Page 58
Adding

1. £400 + £800 + £700 + £500 + £600
   = £3000
2. £500 + £900 + £300 + £700 + £800
   = £3200
3. £300 + £800 + £400 = £1500
4. £200 + £300 + £800 + £400 + £500
   = £2200
5. £100 + £700 + £900 + £300 = £2000
6. £800 + £200 + £400 + £500 = £1900
7. $45 + 38 + 27 + 35 = 145$
8. $37 + 45 + 82 + 38 = 202$
9. $57 + 28 + 32 + 65 = 182$
10. $24 + 29 + 56 + 31 = 140$
11. $27 + 73 + 66 + 42 = 208$
12. $43 + 79 + 21 + 64 = 207$
Owl Answers may vary.

Page 59
Adding

1. $123 + 100 = 223$
   $123 + 99 = 222$
2. $276 - 100 = 176$
   $276 - 98 = 178$
3. $452 + 200 = 652$
   $452 + 198 = 650$
4. $807 - 500 = 307$
   $807 - 499 = 308$
5. $643 + 100 = 743$
   $643 + 103 = 746$
6. $876 - 100 = 776$
   $876 - 102 = 774$
7. $5246 + 3000 = 8246$
   $5246 + 2997 = 8243$
8. $3782 - 2000 = 1782$
   $3782 - 1996 = 1786$
9. $6130 + 400 = 6530$
   $6130 + 399 = 6529$

10. $7423 - 1000 = 6423$
    $7423 - 1006 = 6417$
11. $2106 - 700 = 1406$
    $2106 - 701 = 1405$
12. $4327 + 300 = 4627$
    $4327 + 296 = 4623$
13. $6428 - 300 = 6128$
    $6428 - 299 = 6129$
14. $4832 + 200 = 5032$
    $4832 + 202 = 5034$
15. $8506 - 400 = 8106$
    $8506 - 398 = 8108$
16. 387 g; 0·387 kg
17. 8·24 miles
18. £18
Owl Answers may vary.

Page 60
Adding and subtracting

1. £5·52 – £3 = £2·52
   £2·52 + 1p = £2·53
2. £6·17 – £2 = £4·17
   £4·17 + 1p = £4·18
3. £4·87 – £3 = £1·87
   £1·87 + 1p = £1·88
4. £6·74 – £4 = £2·74
   £2·74 + 1p = £2·75
5. £5·28 – £3 = £2·28
   £2·28 + 1p = £2·29
6. £8·48 – £3 = £5·48
   £5·48 – 2p = £5·46
7. £12·58 – £5 = £7·58
   £7·58 + 2p = £7·60
8. £9·27 – £4 = £5·27
   £5·27 – 1p = £5·26
9. £7·34 – £4 = £3·34
   £3·34 + 3p = £3·37
10. £8·65 – £3 = £5·65
    £5·65 + 3p = £5·68
11. £9·47 – £5 = £4·47
    £4·47 + 3p = £4·50
12. £10·73 – £4 = £6·73
    £6·73 + 4p = £6·77

Explore Answers may vary. Children should notice that the last two digits in the answer are each one more in value than the last two digits of the original number. The digital root of the answer is usually 1 more than the digital root of the original number; the only exception to this is when the digital root of the original number is 9, the digital root of the answer will be 1 (because it will have come out as 1 more than 9, i.e. 10, which then becomes 1).

Page 61

Subtracting

1. £3·46 £4 £10
     \ /   \ /
    54p   £6
   £6·54 to go

2. £15·17 £16 £20
      \ /   \ /
     83p   £4
   £4·83 to go

3. £8·34 £9 £10
     \ /   \ /
    66p   £1
   £1·66 to go

4. £28·28 £29 £30
      \ /   \ /
     72p   £1
   £1·72 to go

5. £16·37 £17 £20
      \ /   \ /
     63p   £3
   £3·63 to go

6. £22·64 £23 £30
      \ /   \ /
     36p   £7
   £7·36 to go

7. £17·42 £18 £20
      \ /   \ /
     58p   £2
   £2·58 to go

8. £6·93 £7 £10
     \ /   \ /
    7p   £3
   £3·07 to go

9. £12·45 £13 £20
      \ /   \ /
     55p   £7
   £7·55 to go

10. £26·76 £27 £30
       \ /   \ /
      24p   £3
   £3·24 to go

11. £14·66 £15 £20
       \ /   \ /
      34p   £5
   £5·34 to go

12. £12·58 £13 £20
       \ /   \ /
      42p   £7
   £7·42 to go

13. £3·86 £4 £5·40
      \ /   \ /
     14p £1·40 £1·54

14. £4·63 £5 £7·20
      \ /   \ /
     37p £2·20 £2·57

15. £3·74 £4 £6·10
      \ /   \ /
     26p £2·10 £2·36

16. £5·84 £6 £8·70
      \ /   \ /
     16p £2·70 £2·86

17. £2·67 £3 £6·30
      \ /   \ /
     33p £3·30 £3·63

18. £3·76 £4 £7·60
      \ /   \ /
     24p £3·60 £3·84

19. £2·45 £3 £5·30
      \ /   \ /
     55p £2·30 £2·85

20. £1·73   £2   £4·20
     \/   \/
     27p   £2·20   £2·47

21. £4·66   £5   £8·50
     \/   \/
     34p   £3·50   £3·84

22. £4·25   £5   £8·16
     \/   \/
     75p   £3·16   £3·91

Owl After ten subtractions you are left
with 55p.

Page 62
Subtracting

1. 2·85   3   7·53
    \/   \/
    0·15   4·53   4·68 m

2. 3·46   4   6·14
    \/   \/
    0·54   2·14   2·68 m

3. 2·65   3   8·23
    \/   \/
    0·35   5·23   5·58 m

4. 3·69   4   4·37
    \/   \/
    0·31   0·37   0·68 m

5. 2·84   3   6·75
    \/   \/
    0·16   3·75   3·91 m

6. 3·28   4   5·43
    \/   \/
    0·72   1·43   2·15 m

7. 4·51   5   5·62
    \/   \/
    0·49   0·62   1·11 m

8. 3·86   4   6·74
    \/   \/
    0·14   2·74   2·88 m

9. 2·49   3   8·37
    \/   \/
    0·51   5·37   5·88 m

10. 678   700   1000
     \/   \/   \
     22   300   472   794
     1472 − 678 = 794
     14·72 − 6·78 = 7·94

11. 865   900   2000
     \/   \/   \
     35   1100   312   1447
     2312 − 865 = 1447
     23·12 − 8·65 = 14·47

12. 764   800   1000
     \/   \/   \
     36   200   414   650
     1414 − 764 = 650
     14·14 − 7·64 = 6·5

13. 945   1000   2000
     \/   \/   \
     55   1000   138   1193
     2138 − 945 = 1193
     21·38 − 9·45 = 11·93

14. 763   800   1000
     \/   \/   \
     37   200   954   1191
     1954 − 763 = 1191
     19·54 − 7·63 = 11·91

15. 654   700   1000
     \/   \/   \
     46   300   837   1183
     1837 − 654 = 1183
     18·37 − 6·54 = 11·83

16. 884   900   2000
     \/   \/   \
     16   1100   276   1392
     2276 − 884 = 1392
     22·76 − 8·84 = 13·92

17. 936   1000
     \/   \
     64   725   789
     1725 − 936 = 789
     17·25 − 9·36 = 7·89

18. 779   800   2000
     \/   \/   \
     21   1200   168   1389
     2168 − 779 = 1389
     21·68 − 7·79 = 13·89

Owl Answers may vary. Children should
notice that the middle digit is
always 9.

Page 63
Subtracting

1. $8342 - 6997 = 1345$
   $8342 - 3676 = 4666$
   $8342 - 5643 = 2699$
   $8342 - 7638 = 704$
   $7368 - 6997 = 371$
   $7368 - 5643 = 1725$
   $7368 - 3676 = 3692$
   $6997 - 5643 = 1354$
   $6997 - 3676 = 3321$
   $5643 - 3676 = 1967$
2. $4{\cdot}45 - 2{\cdot}68 = 1{\cdot}77$
3. $1{\cdot}34 - 0{\cdot}99 = 0{\cdot}35$
4. $5{\cdot}67 - 2{\cdot}34 = 3{\cdot}33$
5. $3{\cdot}26 - 1{\cdot}77 = 1{\cdot}49$
6. $3{\cdot}45 - 1{\cdot}99 = 1{\cdot}46$
7. $8{\cdot}12 - 4{\cdot}8 = 3{\cdot}32$
8. $7{\cdot}2 - 5{\cdot}43 = 1{\cdot}77$
9. $9{\cdot}58 - 4{\cdot}48 = 5{\cdot}1$
10. $7{\cdot}01 - 1{\cdot}82 = 5{\cdot}19$
11. $7{\cdot}68 - 5{\cdot}3 = 2{\cdot}38$
12. $4{\cdot}49 - 2{\cdot}51 = 1{\cdot}98$
13. $0{\cdot}6 - 0{\cdot}32 = 0{\cdot}28$
Owl Answers may vary.

Page 64
Subtracting

1. £3·42; 5 coins
2. 23·9 miles
3. 137 leisure days; 10 weeks
4. $314 - 198 = 116$ fish
5. $207 - 86 = 121$ fish
6. $426 - 264 = 162$ fish
7. $176 - 88 = 88$ fish
8. $324 - 147 = 177$
9. $231 - 169 = 62$
10. 1·74
11. 0·82
12. 2·74
13. 2·24
14. 5·22
15. 3·25
Owl Answers may vary.

Block EI
Page 65
Multiplying and dividing

1. double £43 = £80 + £6 = £86
2. double £54 = £100 + £8 = £108
3. double £72 = £140 + £4 = £144
4. double £84 = £160 + £8 = £168
5. double £37 = £60 + £14 = £74
6. double £29 = £40 + £18 = £58
7. double £69 = £120 + £18 = £138
8. double £87 = £160 + £14 = £174
9. double £78 = £140 + £16 = £156

May be some variation in the way the following answers are broken down:

10. half of £48 = £20 + £4 = £24
11. half of £64 = £30 + £2 = £32
12. half of £78 = £35 + £4 = £39
13. half of £164 = £80 + £2 = £82
14. half of £116 = £50 + £8 = £58
15. half of £152 = £75 + £1 = £76
16. half of £134 = £65 + £2 = £67
17. half of £178 = £85 + £4 = £89
18. half of £196 = £95 + £3 = £98
Owl Answers may vary.

Page 66
Multiplying and dividing

1.

34	150	68	96	46
84	174	54	32	112
76	72	146	128	176
98	108	164	182	52

2.

36	57	24	69	37
63	42	76	48	18
65	86	28	94	51
97	44	83	46	61

3. 480
4. 660
5. 960
6. 1280
7. 1660
8. 1540
9. 1180
10. 920
11. 1760
12. 420
13. 340
14. 435
15. 625
16. 745
17. 765
18. 885
19. 695
20. 590
Owl 480

Page 67
Multiplying and dividing

1. 1530
2. 3400
3. 480
4. 250
5. 640
6. 700
7. 2350
8. 17 000
9. 8350
10. 4850
11. 3900
12. 5750
13. 3850
14. 6350
Owl Answers may vary.
Explore Answers may vary.

Page 68
Multiplying and dividing

1. 1900 people
   £7600

2. 2300 people
   £9200
3. 3900 people
   £15 600
4. 1·9 m
5. 2·3 m
6. 1·4 m
7. 4·2 m
8. 4·6 m
9. 3·9 m
10. 0·6 m
11. 1·7 m
12. 4·8 m
Cut into quarters:
4. 0·95 m
5. 1·15 m
6. 0·7 m
7. 2·1 m
8. 2·3 m
9. 1·95 m
10. 0·3 m
11. 0·85 m
12. 2·4 m
13. half of 15·6 = 7·8
14. half of 9·4 = 4·7
15. double 4·4 = 8·8
16. half of 19·6 = 9·8
17. double 3·7 = 7·4
18. double 2·9 = 5·8
Difference:
13. 0·6
14. 0·1
15. 0·2
16. 0·4
17. 0·5
18. 0·1
Owl Answers may vary.

Page 69
Multiplying by 50 and 25

1. 13 × 100 = 1300
   13 × 50 = 650
2. 22 × 100 = 2200
   22 × 50 = 1100

3. 38 × 100 = 3800
   38 × 50 = 1900
4. 17 × 100 = 1700
   17 × 50 = 850
5. 41 × 100 = 4100
   41 × 50 = 2050
6. 27 × 100 = 2700
   27 × 50 = 1350
7. 35 × 100 = 3500
   35 × 50 = 1750
8. 19 × 100 = 1900
   19 × 50 = 950
9. 24 × 100 = 2400
   24 × 50 = 1200
10. 16 × 100 = 1600
    16 × 50 = 800
    16 × 25 = 400
11. 34 × 100 = 3400
    34 × 50 = 1700
    34 × 25 = 850
12. 28 × 100 = 2800
    28 × 50 = 1400
    28 × 25 = 700
13. 22 × 100 = 2200
    22 × 50 = 1100
    22 × 25 = 550
14. 36 × 100 = 3600
    36 × 50 = 1800
    36 × 25 = 900
15. 44 × 100 = 4400
    44 × 50 = 2200
    44 × 25 = 1100
16. 58 × 100 = 5800
    58 × 50 = 2900
    58 × 25 = 1450
17. 64 × 100 = 6400
    64 × 50 = 3200
    64 × 25 = 1600
18. 72 × 100 = 7200
    72 × 50 = 3600
    72 × 25 = 1800

Owl Times by 100 and then halve 3 times.

Page 70
Double one and halve the other

1. 14 × 35 = 7 × 70 = 490
2. 12 × 15 = 6 × 30 = 180
3. 16 × 25 = 8 × 50 = 400
4. 18 × 25 = 9 × 50 = 450
5. 16 × 30 = 8 × 60 = 480
6. 35 × 18 = 70 × 9 = 630
7. 45 × 12 = 90 × 6 = 540
8. 40 × 18 = 80 × 9 = 720
9. 15 × 16 = 30 × 8 = 240
10. A = 15 × 14 = 30 × 7 = 210 cm^2
11. A = 16 × 25 = 8 × 50 = 400 cm^2
12. A = 18 × 45 = 9 × 90 = 810 cm^2
13. A = 14 × 25 = 7 × 50 = 350 cm^2
14. A = 55 × 12 = 110 × 6 = 660 cm^2
15. A = 12 × 35 = 6 × 70 = 420 cm^2

Explore Answers may vary.

Page 7I
Use facts to find other facts

1.

6	12	18	24	30	36	42	48	54	60
12	24	36	48	60	72	84	96	108	120
24	48	72	96	120	144	168	192	216	240

2. 3 × 24 = 72
3. 7 × 24 = 168
4. 9 × 24 = 216
5. 6 × 24 = 144
6. 8 × 24 = 192
7. 4 × 24 = 96
8. 3 × 13 = 39
9. 12 × 16 = 192
10. 5 × 13 = 65
11. 3 × 15 = 45
12. 7 × 13 = 91
13. 21 × 16 = 336
14. 11 × 13 = 143
15. 5 × 15 = 75
16. 11 × 16 = 176
17. 17 × 15 = 255

18. $17 \times 13 = 221$
19. $16 \times 17 = 272$
20. $13 \times 13 = 169$
21. $6 \times 15 = 90$
22. $16 \times 25 = 400$
23. $24 \times 13 = 312$
24. $18 \times 13 = 234$
25. $13 \times 15 = 195$
26. $31 \times 13 = 403$
27. $11 \times 15 = 165$
Owl $1 \times 17 = 17$
$2 \times 17 = 34$
$4 \times 17 = 68$
$8 \times 17 = 136$
$16 \times 17 = 272$

Page 72
Use facts to find other facts

1. $14 \times 15 = 210$
$7 \times 15 = 105$
2. $35 \times 44 = 1540$
$22 \times 35 = 770$
3. $16 \times 24 = 384$
$8 \times 48 = 384$
4. $48 \times 30 = 1440$
$24 \times 30 = 720$
5. $48 \times 30 = 1440$
$48 \times 15 = 720$
6. $35 \times 44 = 1540$
$35 \times 88 = 3080$
7. $16 \times 24 = 384$
$32 \times 24 = 768$
8. $48 \times 30 = 1440$
$30 \times 96 = 2880$
9. $48 \times 30 = 1440$
$60 \times 48 = 2880$
10. $36 \times 25 = 900$
$72 \times 25 = 1800$
11. $48 \times 30 = 1440$
$24 \times 60 = 1440$
12. $14 \times 15 = 210$
$28 \times 15 = 420$
13. $35 \times 44 = 1540$
$22 \times 70 = 1540$

14. $16 \times 24 = 384$
$48 \times 16 = 768$
15. $48 \times 30 = 1440$
$96 \times 60 = 5760$
16. $36 \times 25 = 900$
$18 \times 50 = 900$
Answers to questions 17–22 may vary.
Owl 48 96 144 192 240 288
336 384 432 480

Page 73
Mixed numbers and improper fractions

1. $2\frac{5}{6}$
2. $3\frac{3}{4}$
3. $2\frac{1}{3}$
4. $4\frac{5}{8}$
5. $3\frac{2}{5}$
6. $1\frac{7}{10}$
7. $1\frac{8}{9}$
8. $5\frac{1}{2}$
9. $3\frac{7}{12}$
10. 7
11. 10
12. 17
13. 17
14. 7
15. 30
16. 34
17. 23
18. 27
19. 13
20. 31
21. 27
22. 7
23. 11
24. 23
Owl 100 minutes = $1\frac{2}{3}$ hours;
150 minutes = $2\frac{1}{2}$ hours;
200 minutes = $3\frac{1}{3}$ hours;
10 days = $1\frac{3}{7}$ weeks;
20 days = $2\frac{6}{7}$ weeks;
30 days = $4\frac{2}{7}$ weeks.

Page 74
Mixed numbers and improper fractions

1. $\frac{13}{3} = 4\frac{1}{3}$ teams
2. $\frac{32}{5} = 6\frac{2}{5}$ teams
3. $\frac{57}{10} = 5\frac{7}{10}$ teams
4. $\frac{43}{4} = 10\frac{3}{4}$ teams
5. $\frac{51}{6} = 8\frac{3}{6}$ (or $\frac{1}{2}$) teams
6. $\frac{63}{8} = 7\frac{7}{8}$ teams
7. $\frac{57}{9} = 6\frac{3}{9}$ (or $\frac{1}{3}$) teams
8. $\frac{41}{7} = 5\frac{6}{7}$ teams
9. $\frac{80}{11} = 7\frac{3}{11}$ teams
10. $\frac{13}{3}$
11. $\frac{27}{5}$
12. $\frac{7}{4}$
13. $\frac{34}{5}$
14. $\frac{23}{8}$
15. $\frac{17}{10}$
16. $\frac{26}{7}$
17. $\frac{11}{6}$
18. $\frac{35}{8}$
19. $\frac{35}{3}$
20. $\frac{57}{4}$
21. $\frac{77}{9}$
22. $\frac{44}{12}$
23. $\frac{82}{11}$
24. $\frac{113}{9}$
25. $\frac{103}{15}$

Owl 1, 4, 8
Explore Answers may vary.

Page 75
Mixed numbers and improper fractions

1. $41 \div 5 = 8\frac{1}{5}$
2. $28 \div 3 = 9\frac{1}{3}$
3. $19 \div 4 = 4\frac{3}{4}$
4. $32 \div 7 = 4\frac{4}{7}$
5. $57 \div 5 = 11\frac{2}{5}$
6. $71 \div 6 = 11\frac{5}{6}$
7. $44 \div 6 = 7\frac{2}{6}$ (or $\frac{1}{3}$)
8. $67 \div 7 = 9\frac{4}{7}$
9. $53 \div 6 = 8\frac{5}{6}$
10. 8
11. 4
12. 11
13. 4
14. 6
15. 4
16. 87
17. 5
18. 4
19. 39
20. 2
21. 3
Explore Answers may vary.

Page 76
Mixed numbers and improper fractions

1. 30
2. 28
3. 44
4. 34
5. 58
6. 30
7. 27
8. 86
9. 36
10. 95
11. 2
12. 4
13. $4\frac{1}{5}$ (or $\frac{2}{4}$) or $3\frac{1}{5}$ (or $\frac{2}{4}$)
14. $\frac{7}{3}$
15. Answers may vary.
Explore Answers may vary.

Page 77
Equivalent fractions

1. $\frac{9}{12} = \frac{3}{4}$
2. $\frac{8}{10} = \frac{4}{5}$

3. $\frac{6}{9} = \frac{2}{3}$

4. $\frac{12}{18} = \frac{2}{3}$

5. $\frac{15}{40} = \frac{3}{8}$

6. $\frac{20}{24} = \frac{5}{6}$

7. $\frac{18}{30} = \frac{3}{5}$

8. $\frac{21}{28} = \frac{3}{4}$

9. $\frac{14}{42} = \frac{1}{3}$

10. $\frac{36}{100} = \frac{9}{25}$

11. $\frac{24}{50} = \frac{12}{25}$

12. $\frac{49}{63} = \frac{7}{9}$

13. $\frac{3}{5} = \frac{6}{10}$

14. $\frac{4}{7} = \frac{12}{21}$

15. $\frac{5}{9} = \frac{20}{36}$

16. $\frac{2}{3} = \frac{16}{24}$

17. $\frac{15}{40} = \frac{3}{8}$

18. $\frac{35}{42} = \frac{5}{6}$

19. $\frac{1}{9} = \frac{8}{72}$

20. $\frac{7}{5} = \frac{28}{20}$

21. $\frac{4}{3} = \frac{28}{21}$

22. $\frac{21}{28} = \frac{3}{4}$

23. $\frac{25}{45} = \frac{5}{9}$

24. $\frac{7}{8} = \frac{42}{48}$

Owl Answers may vary.

Page 78
Ordering fractions

1. $\frac{5}{12}, \frac{5}{6}$

2. $\frac{3}{5}, \frac{2}{3}$

3. $\frac{5}{6}, \frac{7}{8}$

4. $\frac{5}{12}, \frac{3}{4}, \frac{5}{6}$

5. $\frac{7}{15}, \frac{1}{2}, \frac{4}{5}$

6. $\frac{2}{21}, \frac{1}{7}, \frac{2}{3}$

7. $\frac{5}{18}, \frac{4}{9}, \frac{1}{2}$

8. $\frac{1}{2}, \frac{3}{5}, \frac{7}{10}$

9. $\frac{7}{12}, \frac{19}{24}, \frac{5}{6}$

10. $\frac{1}{3}, \frac{17}{30}, \frac{4}{5}$

11. $\frac{3}{8}, \frac{15}{24}, \frac{2}{3}$

12. $\frac{1}{5}, \frac{5}{6}, \frac{27}{30}$

13. true

14. true

15. true

16. false

17. true

18. false

19. true

Owl Answers may vary.

Page 79
Ordering fractions

1. $\frac{10}{12}$ c

2. $\frac{3}{12}$ d

3. $\frac{9}{12}$ g

4. $\frac{2}{12}$ b

5. $\frac{4}{12}$ f

6. $\frac{6}{12}$ e

7. $\frac{8}{12}$ a

8. $\frac{5}{12}$ h

9. true

10. true

11. true

12. true

13. true

14. true

15. false

16. true

17. true

Owl Answers may vary.

Page 80
Ordering fractions

1. $\frac{1}{2} = \frac{15}{30}, \frac{1}{3} = \frac{10}{30}, \frac{2}{5} = \frac{12}{30}$
$\frac{1}{3}, \frac{2}{5}, \frac{1}{2}$

2. $\frac{2}{3} = \frac{20}{30}, \frac{3}{5} = \frac{18}{30}, \frac{7}{10} = \frac{21}{30}$
$\frac{3}{5}, \frac{2}{3}, \frac{7}{10}$

3. $\frac{3}{5} = \frac{18}{30}, \frac{1}{2} = \frac{15}{30}, \frac{5}{6} = \frac{25}{30}$
$\frac{1}{2}, \frac{3}{5}, \frac{5}{6}$

4. $\frac{13}{15} = \frac{26}{30}, \frac{4}{5} = \frac{24}{30}, \frac{7}{10} = \frac{21}{30}$
$\frac{7}{10}, \frac{4}{5}, \frac{13}{15}$

5. $\frac{8}{10} = \frac{24}{30}, \frac{2}{3} = \frac{20}{30}, \frac{4}{5} = \frac{24}{30}$
$\frac{2}{3}, \frac{4}{5}, \frac{8}{10}$ (or $\frac{8}{10}, \frac{4}{5}$)

6. $\frac{3}{15} = \frac{6}{30}, \frac{3}{5} = \frac{18}{30}, \frac{1}{2} = \frac{15}{30}$
$\frac{3}{15}, \frac{1}{2}, \frac{3}{5}$

7. $\frac{12}{60} = \frac{6}{30}, \frac{2}{15} = \frac{4}{30}, \frac{4}{6} = \frac{20}{30}$
$\frac{2}{15}, \frac{12}{60}, \frac{4}{6}$

8. $\frac{1}{2} = \frac{7}{14}, \frac{4}{7} = \frac{8}{14}$
$\frac{1}{2} < \frac{4}{7}$

9. $\frac{2}{3} = \frac{16}{24}, \frac{5}{8} = \frac{15}{24}$
$\frac{2}{3} > \frac{5}{8}$

10. $\frac{2}{5} = \frac{8}{20}, \frac{1}{4} = \frac{5}{20}$
$\frac{2}{5} > \frac{1}{4}$

11. $\frac{5}{6} = \frac{5}{6}, \frac{2}{3} = \frac{4}{6}$
$\frac{5}{6} > \frac{2}{3}$

12. $\frac{2}{3} = \frac{8}{12}, \frac{3}{4} = \frac{9}{12}$
$\frac{2}{3} < \frac{3}{4}$

13. $\frac{7}{9} = \frac{14}{18}, \frac{1}{2} = \frac{9}{18}$
$\frac{7}{9} > \frac{1}{2}$

14. $\frac{2}{5} = \frac{6}{15}, \frac{1}{3} = \frac{5}{15}$
$\frac{2}{5} > \frac{1}{3}$

15. $\frac{3}{4} = \frac{6}{8}, \frac{1}{2} = \frac{4}{8}, \frac{7}{8} = \frac{7}{8}$
$\frac{7}{8} > \frac{3}{4} > \frac{1}{2}$

Owl Answers may vary.

Block AI

Page 3
Rounding

1. (a) 6560 → 7000
   (b) 6360 → 6000
   (c) 6910 → 7000
   (d) 6170 → 6000
   (e) 6730 → 7000
2. (f) 5311 → 5300
   (g) 5347 → 5300
   (h) 5372 → 5400
   (i) 5334 → 5300
   (j) 5388 → 5400
3. (k) 2752 → 2750
   (l) 2789 → 2790
   (m) 2719 → 2720
   (n) 2774 → 2770
   (o) 2737 → 2740
4. (a) £8146 → £8000
   (b) £8100
   (c) £8150
5. (a) £7234 → £7000
   (b) £7200
   (c) £7230
6. (a) 3974 → £4000
   (b) £4000
   (c) £3970
7. (a) £9148 → £9000
   (b) £9100
   (c) £9150
8. (a) £5158 → £5000
   (b) £5200
   (c) £5160
9. (a) £11 762 → £12 000
   (b) £11 800
   (c) £11 760
10. (a) £12 349 → £12 000
    (b) £12 300
    (c) £12 350

11. (a) £6695 → £7000
    (b) £6700
    (c) £6700
12. (a) £15 685 → £16 000
    (b) £15 700
    (c) £15 690
Owl Answers may vary. Answers include any 4-digit numbers ending in the range 995–004, e.g. 1995–2004.

Page 4
Rounding

1. 4328 → (a) 4300 (b) 4330
2. 6795 → (a) 6800 (b) 6800
3. 3827 → (a) 3800 (b) 3830
4. 13 452 → (a) 13 500 (b) 13 450
5. 11 261 → (a) 11 300 (b) 11 260
6. 8875 → (a) 8900 (b) 8880
7. 6983 → (a) 7000 (b) 6980
8. 8914 → (a) 8900 (b) 8910
9. 9276 → (a) 9300 (b) 9280
10. 15 600
11. 12 700
12. 18 200
13. 20 200
14. 15 900
15. 13 600
Explore
10. 4300 + 11 300 = 15 600
11. 8900 + 3800 = 12 700
12. 9300 + 8900 = 18 200
13. 6800 + 13 500 = 20 300
14. 7000 + 8900 = 15 900
15. 4300 + 9300 = 13 600

Page 5
Rounding

1. 27 564 → (a) 28 000 (b) 27 600
2. 18 546 → (a) 19 000 (b) 18 500

3.   43 582 → (a) 44 000   (b) 43 600
4.   13 712 → (a) 14 000   (b) 13 700
5.   64 789 → (a) 65 000   (b) 64 800
6.   34 358 → (a) 34 000   (b) 34 400
7.   10 499 → 10 500; £31 497
8.   £14 000
9.   (a) 3650
     (b) 3749
10. (a) 74 500
     (b) 75 499
11. (a) 4855
     (b) 4864
12. (a) 468 500
     (b) 469 499
13. (a) 58 650
     (b) 58 749
14. (a) 47 385
     (b) 47 394
Owl Answers may vary.

Page 6

Rounding

1.   148 732 → 149 000
2.   154 917 → 155 000
3.   453 281 → 453 000
4.   935 428 → 935 000
5.   347 265 → 347 000
6.   462 842 → 463 000
7.   293 941 → 294 000
8.   392 584 → 393 000
9.   679 325 → 679 000
10. 7 × 3000 = 21 000
11. 3 × 4000 = 12 000
12. 9000 − 3000 = 6000
13. 5000 + 4000 = 9000
14. 9000 ÷ 2 = 4500
15. 5000 ÷ 5 = 1000
16. 7000 + 5000 − 3000 = 9000
17. 4 × 4000 = 16 000
18. 2000 × 8 = 16 000
Explore Answers may vary.

Page 7

Rounding decimals

1.   (a) 4·42 → (a) 4   (b) 4·4
     (b) 4·72 → (a) 5   (b) 4·7
     (c) 4·08 → (a) 4   (b) 4·1
     (d) 4·57 → (a) 5   (b) 4·6
     (e) 4·18 → (a) 4   (b) 4·2
     (f) 4·84 → (a) 5   (b) 4·8
2.   (g) 26·29 → (a) 26   (b) 26·3
     (h) 26·94 → (a) 27   (b) 26·9
     (i) 26·45 → (a) 26   (b) 26·5
     (j) 26·78 → (a) 27   (b) 26·8
     (k) 26·14 → (a) 26   (b) 26·1
     (l) 26·62 → (a) 27   (b) 26·6
3.   34·62 m → (a) 35 m   (b) 34·6 m
4.   18·49 m → (a) 18 m   (b) 18·5 m
5.   13·27 m → (a) 13 m   (b) 13·3 m
6.   25·34 m → (a) 25 m   (b) 25·3 m
7.   11·08 m → (a) 11 m   (b) 11·1 m
8.   19·46 m → (a) 19 m   (b) 19·5 m
9.   26·23 m → (a) 26 m   (b) 26·2 m
10. 42·39 m → (a) 42 m   (b) 42·4 m
11. 20·06 m → (a) 20 m   (b) 20·1 m
Owl Smallest difference = 5·01 m;
     Largest difference = 6·99 m

Page 8

Rounding decimals

1.   £8·38   → (a) £8   (b) £8·40
2.   £14·52 → (a) £15   (b) £14·50
3.   £26·35 → (a) £26   (b) £26·40
4.   £9·18   → (a) £9   (b) £9·20
5.   £32·41 → (a) £32   (b) £32·40
6.   £18·76 → (a) £19   (b) £18·80
7.   £48·48 → (a) £48   (b) £48·50
8.   £32·91 → (a) £33   (b) £32·90
9.   £16·85 → (a) £17   (b) £16·90
10. £25·36 → (a) £25   (b) £25·40
11. £17·18 → (a) £17   (b) £17·20
12. £42·67 → (a) £43   (b) £42·70
13. £58·76 → (a) £59   (b) £58·80
14. £47·43 → (a) £47   (b) £47·40

15. £25·23 → (a) £25 (b) £25·20
16. £26·36 → (a) £26 (b) £26·40
17. £73·84 → (a) £74 (b) £73·80
18. £59·85 → (a) £60 (b) £59·90
19. £27·94 → (a) £28 (b) £27·90
20. £59·26 → (a) £59 (b) £59·30
21. £41·59 → (a) £42 (b) £41·60

Owl

13. £58
14. £48
15. £25
16. £26
17. £73
18. £60
19. £28
20. £59
21. £41

Page 9

Rounding decimals

1. 367·36 → (a) 400 (b) 370
                (c) 367 (d) 367·4
2. 909·56 → (a) 900 (b) 910
                (c) 910 (d) 909·6
3. 8·68 → (a) 0 (b) 10 (c) 9 (d) 8·7
4. 446·92 → (a) 400 (b) 450
                (c) 447 (d) 446·9
5. (a) 7·50 (b) 8·49
6. (a) 48·25 (b) 48·34
7. (a) 34·50 (b) 35·49
8. (a) 35·00 (b) 44·99
9. (a) 15·85 (b) 15·94
10. (a) 5·95 (b) 6·04

Explore Answers may vary.

Page 10

Rounding decimals

1. $3 \times 10 = 30$
2. $6 \times 14 = 84$
3. $45 - 15 = 30$
4. $72 + 18 = 90$
5. $19 \div 2 = 9{\cdot}5$
6. $35 \div 5 = 7$
7. $10 + 8 - 3 = 15$

8. $4 \times 7 = 28$
9. $15 \times 6 = 90$
10. $(2 \times 7) + (2 \times 6) = 14 + 12 = 26\,m$
11. $(2 \times 8) + (2 \times 6) = 16 + 12 = 28\,m$
12. $(2 \times 4) + (2 \times 8) = 8 + 16 = 24\,m$
13. $(2 \times 5) + (2 \times 7) = 10 + 14 = 24\,m$
14. $(2 \times 6) + (2 \times 12) = 12 + 24 = 36\,m$
15. $(2 \times 12) + (2 \times 9) = 24 + 18 = 42\,m$

Estimates:

10. $7 \times 6 = 42\,m^2$
        $7{\cdot}32 \times 5{\cdot}6 = 40{\cdot}992\,m^2$
11. $8 \times 6 = 48\,m^2$
        $8{\cdot}47 \times 6{\cdot}29 = 53{\cdot}2763\,m^2$
12. $4 \times 8 = 32\,m^2$
        $3{\cdot}71 \times 8{\cdot}17 = 30{\cdot}3107\,m^2$
13. $5 \times 7 = 35\,m^2$
        $5{\cdot}36 \times 7{\cdot}28 = 39{\cdot}0208\,m^2$
14. $6 \times 12 = 72\,m^2$
        $6{\cdot}39 \times 11{\cdot}51 = 73{\cdot}5489\,m^2$
15. $12 \times 9 = 108\,m^2$
        $12{\cdot}38 \times 9{\cdot}47 = 117{\cdot}2386\,m^2$

Owl Smallest possible area is
        $5{\cdot}5 \times 5{\cdot}5 = 30{\cdot}25\,m^2$; largest
        possible area is $6{\cdot}49 \times 6{\cdot}49$
        $= 42{\cdot}1201\,m^2$

Page II _Page 27_

Decimal numbers

1. 4 tenths
2. 5 hundredths
3. 4 thousandths
4. 8 units
5. 4 hundredths
6. 2 tenths
7. 8 thousandths
8. 7 tenths
9. 1 thousandth
10. 3·75
11. 4·258
12. 6·791
13. 8·324
14. 5·046
15. 7·208
16. 0·345

17.	4·357	8.	(a) 3451 mm
18.	3·684		(b) 345·1 cm
19.	17·916	9.	(a) 2600 mm
20.	25·143		(b) 260 cm
21.	12·269	10.	3·6 kg
22.	3·478	11.	5·75 kg
23.	8·307	12.	4·752 kg
24.	9·042	13.	0·85 kg
Owl Answers may vary.		14.	0·4 kg
		15.	0·08 kg
		16.	1400 g

Page 12

Decimal numbers

1. 65·487
2. 13·864
3. 24·253
4. 46·701
5. 75·302
6. 38·795
7. 8·581, 8·59, 8·593, 8·6, 8·602
8. 4·145, 4·415, 4·451, 4·514, 4·541
9. 0·35, 0·358, 0·38, 0·385, 0·4
10. 2·147, 2·17, 2·174, 2·18, 2·183
11. 3·04, 3·085, 3·09, 3·092, 3·1

Owl Answers may vary.

17. 1350 g
18. 872 g
19. 1472 g
20. 900 g
21. 650 g
22. 4·75 l
23. 5·6 l
24. 0·89 l
25. 1140 ml
26. 2345 ml
27. 80 ml

Owl

1. Approximately 58 hops
2. Approximately 23 hops
3. Approximately 19 hops
4. Approximately 12 hops
5. Approximately 11 hops
6. Approximately 14 hops
7. Approximately 20 hops
8. Approximately 29 hops
9. Approximately 38 hops

Page 13

Decimal numbers

1. (a) 1732 mm
   (b) 173·2 cm
2. (a) 4356 mm
   (b) 435·6 cm
3. (a) 5279 mm
   (b) 527·9 cm
4. (a) 8350 mm
   (b) 835 cm
5. (a) 9070 mm
   (b) 907 cm
6. (a) 7006 mm
   (b) 700·6 cm
7. (a) 5089 mm
   (b) 508·9 cm

Page 14

Decimal numbers

1. 7·31 > 7·04
2. 5·6 < 5·601
3. 3·79 < 3·8
4. 5·20 = 5·2
5. 4·367 < 4·37
6. 0·28 > 0·273
7. 1·46 < 1·5

Textbook 2

8. $3 \cdot 142 > 3 \cdot 124$

9. $12 \cdot 435 < 12 \cdot 453$

10. $8 \cdot 014 < 8 \cdot 13$

11. $4 \cdot 25$

12. $5 \cdot 47$

13. $2 \cdot 325$

14. $4 \cdot 276$

15. $6 \cdot 343$

16. $19 \cdot 34$

17. $5 \cdot 041$

18. $8 \cdot 273$

19. $7 \cdot 157$

Owl Answers may vary.

Explore 24 possible numbers, ranging from $0 \cdot 457$ to $7 \cdot 540$.

Page 15

Factors

1.

1	24
2	12
3	8
4	6

2.

1	30
2	15
3	10
5	6

3.

1	42
2	21
3	14
6	7

4.

1	28
2	14
4	7

5.

1	38
2	19

6.

1	52
2	26
4	13

7.

1	56
2	28
4	14
7	8

8.

1	48
2	24
3	16
4	12
6	8

9.

1	120
2	60
3	40
4	30
5	24
6	20
8	15
10	12

10.

1	108
2	54
3	36
4	27
6	18
9	12

11.

1	130
2	65
5	26
10	13

12.

1	200
2	100
4	50
5	40
8	25
10	20

13. 8: 1 × 8, 2 × 4
14. 12: 1 × 12, 2 × 6, 3 × 4
15. 20: 1 × 20, 2 × 10, 4 × 5
16. 40: 1 × 40, 2 × 20, 4 × 10, 5 × 8
17. 53: 1 × 53
18. 26: 1 × 26, 2 × 13
19. 18: 1 × 18, 2 × 9, 3 × 6
20. 39: 1 × 39, 3 × 13
Owl 12, 18 and 20

Page 16

Factors

1. 14: 1, 2, 7, 14
2. 22: 1, 2, 11, 22
3. 24: 1, 2, 3, 4, 6, 8, 12, 24
4. 30: 1, 2, 3, 5, 6, 10, 15, 30
5. 34: 1, 2, 17, 30
6. 44: 1, 2, 4, 11, 22, 44
7. 45: 1, 3, 5, 9, 15, 45
8. 56: 1, 2, 4, 7, 8, 14, 28, 56
9. false
10. true
11. false
12. true

13. true
14. false
15. true
16. 9
17. 6
18. 14
19. 9
20. 14
21. 23
22. 7
23. 18
Owl Answers may vary.

Page 17

Factors

1. 2, 4
2. 2
3. 2, 8, 4
4. 2, 7, 14
5. 4, 12, 18, 9
6. 4, 12, 8, 18, 9
7. 4, 12, 5
8. 5, 18, 9
9. 9, 25, 64, 16
10. 3 is a factor of 12
4 is a factor of 84
5 is a factor of 75
6 is a factor of 36
11. 7 is a factor of 49
9 is a factor of 63
8 is a factor of 72
5 is a factor of 85
Explore Answers may vary.

Page 18

Factors

1. Five numbers have 4 factors
One number has 6 factors
2. Four numbers have 6 factors
One number has 8 factors

Answers may vary slightly as sometimes there is more than one way to complete the following tables:

3.

	20	12	6
12	4	3	3
6	2	2	6
20	5	4	1

4.

	30	12	60
12	3	4	3
30	5	2	5
60	6	4	6

5.

	16	30	28
24	4	3	2
35	1	5	7
24	8	6	4

6.

	12	24	45
15	3	3	5
36	4	6	9
24	4	8	3

Owl Answers may vary.

Page 19

Multiplying

1.

	20	4
5	100	20

$100 + 20 = 120 \, cm^2$

2.

	10	8
4	40	32

$40 + 32 = 72 \, cm^2$

3.

	20	3
7	140	21

$140 + 21 = 161 \, cm^2$

4.

	20	5
6	120	30

$120 + 30 = 150 \, cm^2$

5.

	10	3
5	50	15

$50 + 15 = 65 \, cm^2$

6.

	20	6
7	140	42

$140 + 42 = 182 \, cm^2$

7.

	10	9
4	40	36

$40 + 36 = 76 \, cm^2$

8.

	20	2
7	140	14

$140 + 14 = 154 \, cm^2$

9.

	10	7
6	60	42

$60 + 42 = 102 \, cm^2$

10. $(4 \times 80) + (4 \times 1)$
$320 + 4 = 324$

11. $(5 \times 60) + (5 \times 3)$
$300 + 15 = 315$

12. $(6 \times 50) + (6 \times 2)$
$300 + 12 = 312$

13. $(3 \times 70) + (3 \times 3)$
$210 + 9 = 219$

14. $(5 \times 20) + (5 \times 8)$
$100 + 40 = 140$

15. $(6 \times 10) + (6 \times 7)$
$60 + 42 = 102$

16. $(4 \times 20) + (4 \times 7)$
$80 + 28 = 108$

17. $(8 \times 20) + (8 \times 3)$
$160 + 24 = 184$

18. $(7 \times 30) + (7 \times 8)$
$210 + 56 = 266$

Owl Largest: $9 \times 87 = 783$;
Smallest: $1 \times 23 = 23$

Page 20
Multiplying

1. $(6 \times 50) + (6 \times 6)$
   $300 + 36 = 336$
2. $(8 \times 30) + (8 \times 7)$
   $240 + 56 = 296$
3. $(5 \times 70) + (5 \times 8)$
   $350 + 40 = 390$
4. $(7 \times 40) + (7 \times 7)$
   $280 + 49 = 329$
5. $(6 \times 60) + (6 \times 4)$
   $360 + 24 = 384$
6. $(7 \times 20) + (7 \times 9)$
   $140 + 63 = 203$
7. $(5 \times 20) + (5 \times 3)$
   $100 + 15 = 115$
8. $(11 \times 30) + (11 \times 2)$
   $330 + 22 = 352$
9. $(8 \times 30) + (8 \times 4)$
   $240 + 32 = 272$
10. $(6 \times 60) + (6 \times 8)$
    $360 + 48 = £408$
11. $(8 \times 70) + (8 \times 2)$
    $560 + 16 = £576$
12. $(7 \times 40) + (7 \times 4)$
    $280 + 28 = £308$
13. $(7 \times 30) + (7 \times 6)$
    $210 + 42 = £252$
14. $(8 \times 60) + (8 \times 4)$
    $480 + 32 = £512$
15. $(6 \times 50) + (6 \times 9)$
    $300 + 54 = £354$
16. $(6 \times 20) + (6 \times 2)$
    $120 + 12 = £132$
17. $(8 \times 80) + (8 \times 7)$
    $640 + 56 = £696$
18. $(7 \times 100) + (7 \times 40) + (7 \times 5)$
    $700 + 280 + 35 = £1015$

Owl Answers may vary. Answers may include the adding together of the x20 and x1 tables, or the x10 and x11 tables.

Page 21
Multiplying

1. $(6 \times 4) + (6 \times 0.7)$
   $24 + 4.2 = 28.2\,ml$
2. $(5 \times 3) + (5 \times 0.6)$
   $15 + 3.0 = 18.0\,ml$
3. $(8 \times 2) + (8 \times 0.5)$
   $16 + 4.0 = 20.0\,ml$
4. $(4 \times 3) + (4 \times 0.4)$
   $12 + 1.6 = 13.6\,ml$
5. $(5 \times 4) + (5 \times 0.8)$
   $20 + 4.0 = 24.0\,ml$
6. $(7 \times 2) + (7 \times 0.8)$
   $14 + 5.6 = 19.6\,ml$
7. $(8 \times 4) + (8 \times 0.5)$
   $32 + 4.0 = 36.0\,ml$
8. $(6 \times 3) + (6 \times 0.7)$
   $18 + 4.2 = 22.2\,ml$
9. $(5 \times 4) + (5 \times 0.4)$
   $20 + 2.0 = 22.0\,ml$
10. $(4 \times 2) + (4 \times 0.6)$
    $8 + 2.4 = 10.4\,ml$
11. $(7 \times 3) + (7 \times 0.8)$
    $21 + 5.6 = 26.6\,ml$
12. $(6 \times 2) + (6 \times 0.9)$
    $12 + 5.4 = 17.4\,ml$
13. $(6 \times 60) + (6 \times 4)$
    $360 + 24 = 384$
    116 more to have 500
14. $(8 \times 50) + (8 \times 6)$
    $400 + 48 = 448$
    $(7 \times 20) + (7 \times 8)$
    $140 + 56 = 196$
    $448 + 196 = 644$
15. $(6 \times 8) + (6 \times 0.6)$
    $48 + 3.6 = 51.6\,l$
    $51.6 \times £1.10 = (51.6 \times 1) + (51.6 \times 0.1)$
    $= 51.6 + 5.16 = £56.76$

Explore Answers may vary.

Page 22

Multiplying

The way some numbers are broken down in questions 1–15 may vary.

1. 18×45
   $9 \times 2 \times 45$
   9×90
   $= 810$
2. 15×35
   $5 \times 3 \times 35$
   5×105
   $= 525$
3. 14×15
   $7 \times 2 \times 15$
   7×30
   $= 210$
4. 18×55
   $9 \times 2 \times 55$
   9×110
   $= 990$
5. 16×27
   $4 \times 4 \times 27$
   4×108
   $= 432$
6. 24×33
   $8 \times 3 \times 33$
   8×99
   $= 792$
7. 15×44
   $3 \times 5 \times 44$
   3×220
   $= 660$
8. 18×42
   $3 \times 6 \times 42$
   3×252
   $= 756$
9. 16×34
   $4 \times 4 \times 34$
   4×136
   $= 544$
10. 15×28
    $3 \times 5 \times 28$
    3×140
    $= 420$
11. 18×38
    $9 \times 2 \times 38$
    9×76
    $= 684$
12. 24×24
    $8 \times 3 \times 24$
    8×72
    $= 576$
13. 18×23
    $9 \times 2 \times 23$
    9×46
    $= 414$
14. 15×29
    $5 \times 3 \times 29$
    5×87
    $= 435$
15. 36×17
    $6 \times 6 \times 17$
    6×102
    $= 612$
16. 330
17. 450
18. 399
19. 368
20. 425
21. 432
22. 418
23. 414
24. 384

Owl Answers may vary.

Page 23

Multiplying

1. $(12 \times 20) + (12 \times 3)$
   $240 + 36 = 276$
2. $(12 \times 20) + (12 \times 7)$
   $240 + 84 = 324$
3. $(12 \times 30) + (12 \times 1)$
   $360 + 12 = 372$
4. $(12 \times 40) + (12 \times 3)$
   $480 + 36 = 516$
5. $(12 \times 30) + (12 \times 5)$
   $360 + 60 = 420$
6. $(12 \times 40) + (12 \times 7)$
   $480 + 84 = 564$

7. $(12 \times 50) + (12 \times 2)$
   $600 + 24 = 624$
8. $(12 \times 40) + (12 \times 2)$
   $480 + 24 = 504$
9. $(12 \times 30) + (12 \times 9)$
   $360 + 108 = 468$
10. $(12 \times 40) + (12 \times 8)$
    $480 + 96 = 576$
11. $(12 \times 30) + (12 \times 3)$
    $360 + 36 = 396$
12. $(12 \times 20) + (12 \times 8)$
    $240 + 96 = 336$
13. $(15 \times 20) + (15 \times 6)$
    $300 + 90 = 390$

Explore Answers may vary.

Page 24
Multiplying

1. $(14 \times 20) + (14 \times 7)$
   $280 + 98 = 378$
2. $(14 \times 30) + (14 \times 6)$
   $420 + 84 = 504$
3. $(14 \times 20) + (14 \times 3)$
   $280 + 42 = 322$
4. $(14 \times 30) + (14 \times 8)$
   $420 + 112 = 532$
5. $(14 \times 40) + (14 \times 2)$
   $560 + 28 = 588$
6. $(14 \times 50) + (14 \times 3)$
   $700 + 42 = 742$
7. $(14 \times 30) + (14 \times 4)$
   $420 + 56 = 476$
8. $(14 \times 40) + (14 \times 5)$
   $560 + 70 = 630$
9. $(24 \times 20) + (24 \times 8)$
   $480 + 192 = 672$
10. $(13 \times 20) + (13 \times 6)$
    $260 + 78 = 338 = £3·38$
11. $(13 \times 30) + (13 \times 4)$
    $390 + 52 = 442 = £4·42$
12. $(13 \times 50) + (13 \times 5)$
    $650 + 65 = 715 = £7·15$
13. $(13 \times 40) + (13 \times 3)$
    $520 + 39 = 559 = £5·59$

14. $(13 \times 30) + (13 \times 7)$
    $390 + 91 = 481 = £4·81$
15. $(13 \times 50) + (13 \times 2)$
    $650 + 26 = 676 = £6·76$
16. $(13 \times 20) + (13 \times 4)$
    $260 + 52 = 312 = £3·12$
17. $(13 \times 40) + (13 \times 8)$
    $520 + 104 = 624 = £6·24$

Owl Answers may vary.

Page 25
Multiplying

1. $23 \times 100 = 2300$
   $23 \times 50 \ = 1150$
   $23 \times 51 \ = 1150 + 23$
   $\qquad\quad = 1173$
2. $76 \times 100 = 7600$
   $76 \times 50 \ = 3800$
   $76 \times 52 \ = 3800 + 152$
   $\qquad\quad = 3952$
3. $43 \times 100 = 4300$
   $43 \times 99 \ = 4300 - 43$
   $\qquad\quad = 4257$
4. $64 \times 100 = 6400$
   $64 \times 101 = 6400 + 64$
   $\qquad\quad = 6464$
5. $38 \times 100 = 3800$
   $38 \times 50 \ = 1900$
   $38 \times 51 \ = 1900 + 38$
   $\qquad\quad = 1938$
6. $73 \times 100 = 7300$
   $73 \times 50 \ = 3650$
   $73 \times 52 \ = 3650 + 146$
   $\qquad\quad = 3796$
7. $26 \times 50 = 1300$
   $26 \times 52 = 1300 + 52 = 1352$
   $1500 - 1352 = 148$
   148 more weeks
8. $23 \times 50 = 1150$
   $23 \times 49 = 1150 - 23$
   $\qquad\quad = 1127$ points in a season
9. $13 \times 50 = 650$
   $13 \times 52 = 650 + 26$
   $\qquad\quad = 676$ shots on target

10. $24 \times 50 = 1200$
$24 \times 49 = 1200 - 24$
$= 1176$

11. $46 \times 50 = 2300$
$46 \times 49 = 2300 - 46$
$= 2254$

12. $37 \times 50 = 1850$
$37 \times 49 = 1850 - 37$
$= 1813$

13. $52 \times 50 = 2600$
$52 \times 49 = 2600 - 52$
$= 2548$

14. $29 \times 50 = 1450$
$29 \times 49 = 1450 - 29$
$= 1421$

15. $41 \times 50 = 2050$
$41 \times 49 = 2050 - 41$
$= 2009$

16. $34 \times 50 = 1700$
$34 \times 49 = 1700 - 34$
$= 1666$

17. $56 \times 50 = 2800$
$56 \times 49 = 2800 - 56$
$= 2744$

18. $32 \times 50 = 1600$
$32 \times 49 = 1600 - 32$
$= 1568$

Page 26

Multiplying

1. $17 \times 63 = 1071$
2. $18 \times 55 = 990$
3. $23 \times 49 = 1127$
4. $15 \times 73 = 1095$
5. $17 \times 54 = 918$
6. $35 \times 35 = 1225$
7. $18 \times 67 = 1206$
8. $13 \times 82 = 1066$
9. $124 \times 12 = 1488$
10. $236 \times 11 = 2596$
11. $42 \times 49 = 2058$
12. $16 \times 46 = 736$
13. $28 \times 75 = 2100$

14. $24 \times 43 = 1032$
15. $49 \times 123 = 6027$
16. $49 \times 68 = 3332$
17. $14 \times 37 = 518$
18. $18 \times 48 = 864$
Explore Answers may vary.

Page 27

Coordinates

1. A $(1, 2)$
B $(1, 4)$
C $(1, 6)$
D $(2, 5)$
E $(3, 4)$
F $(4, 5)$
G $(5, 6)$
H $(5, 4)$
I $(5, 2)$

2.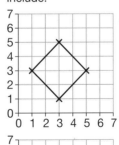

Owl Answers will vary. Possible answers include:

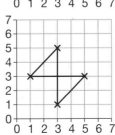

Page 28

Coordinates

1. A (2, 2)
   B (5, 2)
   C (6, 5)
   D (3, 4)
   E (4, 6)
   F (7, 8)
   G (8, 3)
   H (7, 2)
   I (8, 6)
   J (2, 8)
   K (0, 3)
   L (5, 9)
   M (3, 6)
2. 7 units
3. 6 units
4. 5 units
5. 2 units
6. 2 units
7. 5 units
8. 3 units
9. 6 units
10. (5, 6)
11. (6, 8)
12. (0, 2)
13. (9, 2)
14. (1, 8)
15. (6, 3)
16. (6, 2)
17. (7, 5)
18. (3·5, 6)
19. (7·5, 2·5)
20. (2·5, 3)
21. (7, 5·5)
Owl Answers may vary.

Page 29

Coordinates

1. A (1, 1)
   B (3, 3)
   C (2, 5)
   D (⁻2, 1)
   E (⁻3, ⁻2)
   F (⁻4, 5)
   G (2, ⁻3)
   H (5, ⁻2)
   I (⁻1, ⁻5)
Explore Answers may vary. Children
   should notice that, when
   reflecting in the *x*-axis, all the
   y-coordinates become negative.
   When reflecting in the *y*-axis,
   all the *x*-coordinates become
   negative. When reflecting in both
   axes, both sets of coordinates
   change their polarity.

Page 30

3D shapes

1. Cube
   6 faces
2. Tetrahedron
   4 faces
3. Triangular prism
   5 faces
4. Pentagonal prism
   7 faces
5. Cuboid
   6 faces
6. Square-based pyramid
   5 faces
7. Hexagonal prism 8 faces
8.
9.
10.
11.

12.

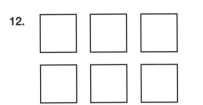

Owl Answers may vary.

Page 3I
3D shapes

1. Cuboid
6 faces

| ×2 | ×2 | ×2 |
| rectangle | rectangle | rectangle |

2. Tetrahedron
4 faces

×4
triangle

3. Octahedron
8 faces

×8
triangle

4. Triangular prism
5 faces

×2   ×3
triangle   rectangle

5. Hexagonal prism
8 faces

×6
rectangle

×2
hexagon

6. Square-based pyramid
5 faces

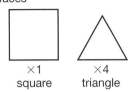

×1   ×4
square   triangle

1. (a) yes
(b) yes
(c) yes
(d) yes

2. (a) no
(b) no
(c) no
(d) no

3. (a) yes
(b) no
(c) yes
(d) yes

4. (a) yes
(b) yes
(c) yes
(d) yes

5. (a) yes
(b) yes
(c) yes
(d) yes

6. (a) no
(b) no
(c) yes
(d) yes

Explore Answers may vary.

Page 32
3D shapes

1. 6 faces
2. 8 faces
3. 6 faces
4. 10 faces
5. 10 faces
6. 12 faces
7. 14 faces
8. a or h

9. a, c, d, h or f
10. i
11. j
12. s
13. r
Owl Answers may vary.

Page 33
3D shapes

1. cube
2. cuboid
3. none
4. square-based pyramid
5. none
6. cube
7. none
8. prism
9. none
10. true
11. true
12. false
13. false
14. true
15. false
16. true
17. true

Block C2
Page 34
Area of rectangles

1. Area = 5 × 3
   = 15 cm^2
2. Area = 4 × 6
   = 24 cm^2
3. Area = 12 × 7
   = 84 cm^2
4. Area = 7·5 × 8
   = 60 m^2
5. Area = 30 × 20
   = 600 mm^2
6. Area = 3·5 × 10
   = 35 cm^2
7. 21 m^2

8. 69 m^2
9. 74 m^2
10. 147 m^2
11. 118 m^2
12. 610 m^2
Perimeter:
7. 20 m
8. 38 m
9. 40 m
10. 56 m
11. 56 m
12. 130 m
Owl Answers may vary. Answers include rectangles with sides: 3 cm by 4 cm, 6 cm by 2 cm, and 12 cm by 1 cm.

Page 35
Area of rectangles

1. 1 cm^2 = 10 × 10 = 100 mm^2
2. 1 m^2 = 100 × 100 = 10 000 cm^2
3. 7 cm^2 = 10 × 70 = 700 mm^2
4. 4000 mm^2 = 40 × 1 = 40 cm^2
5. 4·5 m^2 = 450 × 100 = 45 000 cm^2
6. 60 000 cm^2 = 12 000 × 50 000 = 6 000 000 mm^2
7. 1 km^2 = 1000 × 1000 = 1 000 000 m^2
8. 35 cm^2 = 70 × 50 = 3500 mm^2
9. 4 000 000 mm^2 = 200 × 200 = 40 000 cm^2
10. 6 × 20 = 120 m^2
11. 44 × 18 = 792 m^2
    792 m^2 – 120 m^2 = 672 m^2
12. 50 × 80 = 4000 m^2
    4000 m^2 – 792 m^2 = 3208 m^2
13. 3208 × 2 = 6416 m^2
14. 100 × 18 = 1800 m^2
15. 8000 – 120 = 7880 m^2
Owl 1 lap = 360 m; 2 laps = 720 m; 3 laps = 1080 m; 4 laps = 1440 m; 5 laps = 1800 m; 10 laps = 3600 m. They would need to run 58 $\frac{1}{3}$ laps to cover 21 km; about 14 laps to cover 5 km; and about 28 laps to cover 10 km.

Page 36
Area of rectangles

1. $128\,m^2$
2. $160\,m^2$
3. $119\,m^2$
4. $51\,m^2$
5. $248\,m^2$
6. $69{\cdot}5\,m^2$
7. $A = 28\,mm^2$
8. $L = 12\,cm$
9. $W = 50\,mm$
10. $L = 6\,cm$
11. $2\,cm$ and $6\,cm$
12. $6\,cm$ and $4\,cm$
13. $10\,cm$ and $3\,cm$
14. $6\,cm$ and $8{\cdot}5\,cm$

Owl 4

Page 37
Surface area of cuboids

1. $(2 \times 9) + (2 \times 15) + (2 \times 15)$
$= 18 + 30 + 30 = 78\,cm^2$
2. $(2 \times 8) + (2 \times 28) + (2 \times 14)$
$= 16 + 56 + 28 = 100\,cm^2$
3. $(2 \times 12) + (2 \times 24) + (2 \times 32)$
$= 24 + 48 + 64 = 136\,cm^2$
4. $(2 \times 15) + (2 \times 33) + (2 \times 55)$
$= 30 + 66 + 110 = 206\,cm^2$
5. $(2 \times 24) + (2 \times 32) + (2 \times 48)$
$= 48 + 64 + 96 = 208\,cm^2$
6. $(2 \times 21) + (2 \times 27) + (2 \times 63)$
$= 42 + 54 + 126 = 222\,cm^2$

Explore Answers may vary.

Page 38
Area of right-angled triangles

1. $6 \times 8 = 48$
Area $= 24\,cm^2$
2. $9 \times 5 = 45$
Area $= 22{\cdot}5\,cm^2$
3. $8 \times 12 = 96$
Area $= 48\,cm^2$

4. $8 \times 8 = 64$
Area $= 32\,cm^2$
5. $6 \times 8{\cdot}5 = 51$
Area $= 25{\cdot}5\,cm^2$
6. $7 \times 8 = 56$
Area $= 28\,cm^2$
7. $A = 20\,units^2$
8. $A = 10\,units^2$
9. $A = 5\,units^2$
10. $A = 12\,units^2$
11. $A = 2\,units^2$
12. $A = 3\,units^2$
13. $A = 4{\cdot}5\,units^2$
14. $A = 9\,units^2$

Explore Area $= 8\ cm^2$

Page 39
Area of right-angled triangles

1. Answers may vary. Rectangle should have an area of $24\,cm^2$.
2. Answers may vary. Rectangle should have an area of $56\,cm^2$.
3. Answers may vary. Rectangle should have an area of $30\,cm^2$.
4. Answers may vary. Rectangle should have an area of $15\,cm^2$.
5. $5 \times 6 = 30$
Area $= 15\,cm^2$
6. $4 \times 7 = 28$
Area $= 14\,cm^2$
7. $6{\cdot}5 \times 8 = 52$
Area $= 26\,cm^2$
8. $10 \times 12 = 120$
Area $= 60\,cm^2$
9. $7 \times 9 = 63$
Area $= 31{\cdot}5\,cm^2$
10. $6 \times 13 = 78$
Area $= 39\,cm^2$
11. $(2 \times 5) + (2 \times 4) + (2 \times 3) + (3 \times 4)$
$= 10 + 8 + 6 + 12 = 36\,cm^2$
12. $(3 \times 8) + (3 \times 10) + (3 \times 6) + (8 \times 10)$
$= 24 + 30 + 18 + 80 = 152\,cm^2$

13. $(7 \times 13) + (7 \times 5) + (7 \times 12) + (5 \times 12)$
$= 91 + 35 + 84 + 60 = 270\,cm^2$

Explore Answers may vary.

Page 40

Area of shapes that contain right-angled triangles

1. $A = 2\,cm^2$
2. $A = 6\,cm^2$
3. $A = 7\,cm^2$
4. $A = 12\,cm^2$
5. $A = 8\,cm^2$
6. $A = 2\,cm^2$
7. $A = 6 \cdot 5\,cm^2$
8. $A = 2\,cm^2$
9. $A = 13 \cdot 5\,cm^2$
10. $a = 4\,cm$
11. $b = 6\,cm$
12. $c = 9\,cm$
13. $d = 8\,cm$
14. $A = 1 \cdot 5\,units^2$
15. $A = 3\,units^2$
16. $A = 1\,unit^2$
17. $A = 1 \cdot 5\,units^2$
18. $A = 2\,units^2$

Explore Answers may vary.

Page 4l

Area of non right-angled triangles

1. $4 \times 8 = 32$
$A = 16 + 16 = 32\,cm^2$
2. $5 \times 3 = 15$
$5 \times 6 = 30$
$A = 7 \cdot 5 + 15 = 22 \cdot 5\,cm^2$
3. $7 \cdot 5 \times 4 = 30$
$7 \cdot 5 \times 8 = 60$
$A = 15 + 30 = 45\,cm^2$
4. $9 \times 3 = 27$
$9 \times 7 = 63$
$A = 13 \cdot 5 + 31 \cdot 5 = 45\,cm^2$

5. $6 \cdot 5 \times 12 = 78$
$6 \cdot 5 \times 3 = 19 \cdot 5$
$A = 39 + 9 \cdot 75 = 48 \cdot 75\,cm^2$
6. $A = 24\,cm^2$

Explore

Shape	A	P	I
1	$12\,cm^2$	14	6
2	$4 \cdot 5\,cm^2$	9	1
3	$12\,cm^2$	12	7

Page 42

Averages

1. $6 + 8 = 14$
$14 \div 2 = 7$
2. $7 + 9 = 16$
$16 \div 2 = 8$
3. $8 + 5 = 13$
$13 \div 2 = 6 \cdot 5$
4. $4 + 5 + 6 = 15$
$15 \div 3 = 5$
5. $7 + 10 + 4 = 21$
$21 \div 3 = 7$
6. $3 + 6 + 9 = 18$
$18 \div 3 = 6$
7. $3 + 5 + 5 + 7 = 20$
$20 \div 4 = 5$
8. $4 + 6 + 11 + 3 = 24$
$24 \div 4 = 6$
9. $5 + 10 + 7 + 6 = 28$
$28 \div 4 = 7$
10. $6 + 4 + 8 = 18$
$18 \div 3 = 6$
11. $3 + 3 + 4 + 5 = 15$
$15 \div 4 = 3 \cdot 75$
12. $7 + 7 + 7 = 21$
$21 \div 3 = 7$
13. $8 + 9 = 17$
$17 \div 2 = 8 \cdot 5$
14. $4 + 5 + 7 + 4 = 20$
$20 \div 4 = 5$
15. $5 + 3 + 5 + 4 + 6 = 23$
$23 \div 5 = 4 \cdot 6$

Owl Answers may vary.

Page 43

Averages

1. $5 + 7 + 4 + 7 + 7 = 30$
   $30 \div 5 = 6$
2. $8 + 2 + 7 + 4 + 4 = 25$
   $25 \div 5 = 5$
3. $3 + 2 + 5 + 4 + 4 + 6 = 24$
   $24 \div 6 = 4$
4. $8 + 7 + 7 + 6 = 28$
   $28 \div 4 = 7$
5. $6 + 10 + 8 + 9 + 9 + 9 + 5 = 56$
   $56 \div 7 = 8$
6. $4 + 3 + 6 + 5 + 5 + 7 = 30$
   $30 \div 6 = 5$
7. $6 + 6 + 8 + 7 + 9 + 6 = 42$
   $42 \div 6 = 7$

Best team: Whites

1. (a) 7
   (b) 4–7
2. (a) 4
   (b) 2–8
3. (a) 4
   (b) 2–6
4. (a) 7
   (b) 6–8
5. (a) 9
   (b) 5–10
6. (a) 5
   (b) 3–7
7. (a) 6
   (b) 6–9
8. $2 + 1 + 3 + 7 + 4 + 6 + 5 + 8 + 2 + 1$
   $= 39$
   mean = 3·9
9. $4 + 3 + 4 + 2 + 3 + 4 + 2 + 3 + 4 + 2$
   $= 31$
   mean = 3·1
10. $6 + 6 + 3 + 6 + 3 + 6 + 7 + 10 + 7 + 3$
    $= 57$
    mean = 5·7
11. $9 + 9 + 2 + 8 + 12 + 10 + 3 + 3 + 6$
    $+ 10 = 72$
    mean = 7·2
12. $4 + 4 + 8 + 10 + 4 + 3 + 6 + 9 + 2$
    $+ 7 = 57$
    mean = 5·7
13. $12 + 15 + 11 + 12 + 22 + 13 + 12$
    $+ 9 + 11 + 15 = 132$
    mean = 13·2

In order: Guy, Cho, Peter, Beth, Dan, Ramesh

Owl Answers may vary.

Page 44

Averages

1. 1, 1, 2, 3, 3, 4, 4, 5, 7
   Median = 3
2. 1, 1, 2, 2, 3, 4, 5
   Median = 2
3. 1, 2, 2, 3, 3, 4, 5, 5
   Median = 3
4. 1, 2, 2, 3, 4, 6, 6, 7, 8, 9
   Median = 5
5. 1, 1, 2, 2, 3, 3, 4, 4
   Median = 2·5
6. 2, 3, 5, 5, 5, 5, 5, 5, 6, 7, 9
   Median = 5

Mean:
1. $3\frac{1}{3}$
2. $2\frac{4}{7}$
3. $3\frac{1}{8}$
4. $4\frac{4}{5}$ or $4\frac{8}{10}$
5. $2\frac{1}{2}$
6. $5\frac{2}{11}$

Explore Answers may vary.

Page 45

Averages

1. (a) 6·5°C
   (b) 7°C
   (c) 7°C
2. (a) 6·2°C
   (b) 6°C
   (c) 6°C
3. (a) 19·1°C
   (b) 18°C
   (c) 18·5°C

4. (a) 12·6°C
   (b) 12°C
   (c) 12·5°C

5. (a) 6·5°C
   (b) 6 or 7°C
   (c) 6·5°C

6. (a) 11·5°C
   (b) 12°C
   (c) 11·5°C

7. (a) 27·7°C
   (b) 28°C
   (c) 28°C

8. (a) 34·5°C
   (b) 33°C
   (c) 34·5°C

9. 5
10. 7
11. 7
12. 14
13. 31
14. 30

Explore The mean number of days per month in a year is 365 ÷ 12 = 30·4. The mode is 31 days. The median is 31 days. The only one that changes if it is a leap year is the mean, which = 30·5.

Page 46
Line graphs

1. £4
2. £6
3. £8
4. £16
5. £9
6. £5
7. £11
8. £13
9. 2 months
10. 6 months
11. 1 month
12. $2\frac{1}{2}$ months
13. $6\frac{1}{2}$ months

14. £1 saved after $\frac{1}{2}$ a month; £7 saved after $3\frac{1}{2}$ months; £15 saved after $7\frac{1}{2}$ months

Owl Sunil will have saved £4·50 after 9 weeks; £6·50 after 15 weeks.

Page 47
Line graphs

1. £20
2. £7·50
3. £22·50
4. £11
5. £34
6. £23
7. 40
8. 70
9. 55
10. 62
11. 52

Explore

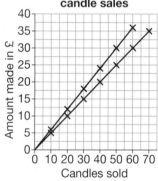

Graph to show Annie's candle sales

Increase in earnings from selling 40 candles = £4. Increase for selling 15 candles = £1·50.

Page 48
Line graphs

1. $32
2. $80
3. $128
4. $112
5. $72

6. $176
7. $320
8. $232
9. $240
10. $1600
11. £20
12. £50
13. £60
14. £40
15. £16·25
16. £200
17. £100
18. £600
19. £5
20. £400
Owl Answers may vary.

Page 4q

Line graphs

x-axis (£)	y-axis (Rupees)
1	80
2	160
3	240
4	320
5	400
6	480
7	560
8	640
9	720
10	800

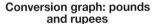
Conversion graph: pounds and rupees

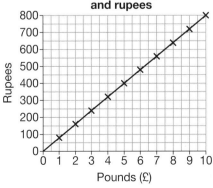

1. £10
2. £3
3. £5·50
4. £6
5. £4·50
6. £20
7. £15
8. £50
9. £2·50
10. 240R
11. 400R
12. 800R
13. 200R
14. 1200R
15. 600R
16. 3200R
Owl 1 000 000R = £12 500

Block D2

Page 50

Adding and subtracting

1. £3·55 – 40p = £3·15
2. £4·25 – 60p = £3·65
3. £6·64 – 33p = £6·31
4. £2·16 – 82p = £1·34
5. £2·35 – 46p = £1·89
6. £5·53 – 27p = £5·26
7. 3·61 – 0·4 = 3·21
8. 4·78 – 0·6 = 4·18
9. 2·74 – 0·7 = 2·04
10. 6·38 – 0·2 = 6·18
11. 4·48 – 0·06 = 4·42
12. 3·65 – 0·3 = 3·35
13. 8·62 – 0·01 = 8·61
14. 5·78 – 0·03 = 5·75
15. 9·97 – 0·5 = 9·47

Owl The two missing numbers can be: 0 and 9, 1 and 8, 2 and 7, 3 and 6, 4 and 5, 5 and 4, 6 and 3, 7 and 2, 8 and 1, or 9 and 0.

Page 51
Adding and subtracting

1. $0.7 + 0.46 = 1.16$
2. $0.5 + 0.72 = 1.22$
3. $0.6 + 0.55 = 1.15$
4. $0.4 + 0.61 = 1.01$
5. $0.5 + 0.64 = 1.14$
6. $0.7 + 0.53 = 1.23$
7. $0.6 + 0.82 = 1.42$
8. $0.4 + 0.76 = 1.16$
9. $0.53 - 0.2 = 0.33$ m
10. $1.73 - 0.4 = 1.33$ m
11. $1.85 - 0.8 = 1.05$ m
12. $0.72 - 0.41 = 0.31$ m
13. $0.66 - 0.53 = 0.13$ m
14. $0.84 - 0.82 = 0.02$ m
15. $1.34 - 0.8 = 0.54$ m
16. $1.46 - 0.41 = 1.05$ m
Owl Answers may vary.

Page 52
Adding and subtracting

1. 2.2
2. 4.8
3. 1.5
4. 4.4
5. 3.1
6. 4.8
7. 3.5
8. 2.4
9. 1.2
10. 0.8
11. 2.9
12. 3.7
13. 6.1
14. 0.4
15. 3.9
16. 0.48 km
17. 0.23 km
18. 1.06 km
19. 1.03 km
20. 2.76 km
21. 0.35 km
Owl One could have run 1.36 km and the other 1.84 km.

Page 53
Adding and subtracting

1. $0.7 - 0.21 = 0.49$
2. $0.9 - 0.48 = 0.42$
3. $0.6 - 0.43 = 0.17$
4. $0.8 - 0.17 = 0.63$
5. $6.42 - 3.31 = 3.11$
6. $4.8 - 1.35 = 3.45$
7. $4.3 + 2.81 = 7.11$
8. $3.72 + 1.46 = 5.18$
9. $7.52 - 4.81 = 2.71$
10. $5.9 - 3.27 = 2.63$
11. $0.8 - 0.63 = 0.17$
12. $1.2 + 0.71 = 1.91$
13. $3.62 - 1.51 = 2.11$
14. $3.9 + 4.71 = 8.61$
15. $1.68 + 3.42 = 5.1$
16. 1.36 m
17. 0.17 kg
18. 1.26 l; 0.96 l
Owl $0.31 - 0.09 = 0.22$; $0.45 - 0.09$
$= 0.36$. The pattern is that the tenths digit will always decrease by 1 and the hundredths digit will always increase by 1.

Page 54
Adding

Estimates may vary.

1. $\boxed{700}$
    364
    $\underline{+\ 358}$
    722
    11

2. (800)
   428
   + 358
   ―――
   786
   1

3. (600)
   236
   + 347
   ―――
   583
   1

4. (725)
   441
   + 275
   ―――
   716
   1

5. (800)
   384
   + 417
   ―――
   801
   1 1

6. (700)
   326
   + 383
   ―――
   709
   1

7. (600)
   328
   + 287
   ―――
   615
   1 1

8. (1050)
   546
   + 484
   ―――
   1030
   1 1

   (1100)
   1030
   + 128
   ―――
   1158

9. (325)
   176
   + 158
   ―――
   334
   1 1

10. (1200)
    562
    + 588
    ―――
    1150
    1 1

11. (1150)
    637
    + 484
    ―――
    1121
    1 1

12. (1000)
    359
    + 642
    ―――
    1001
    1 1

13. (875)
    475
    + 392
    ―――
    867
    1

14. (900)
    584
    + 312
    ―――
    896

15. (1050)
    627
    + 439
    ―――
    1066
    1

16. (1150)
    579
    + 542
    ―――
    1121
    1 1

17. (1100)
    658
    + 463
    ―――
    1121
    1 1

Owl Answers may vary.

Page 55

Adding

Estimates may vary.

1. (9000)
   3426
   + 5878
   9304
   1 1 1

2. (12000)
   3578
   + 8675
   12253
   1 1 1

3. (10000)
   4372
   + 5683
   10055
   1 1

4. (8000)
   6955
   + 1218
   8173
   1 1

5. (8500)
   5289
   + 3476
   8765
   1 1

6. (9500)
   3143
   + 6354
   9497

7. (12000)
   6836
   + 4734
   11570
   1 1

8. (17000)
   7668
   + 8985
   16653
   1 1 1

9. (11000)
   4783
   + 5878
   10661
   1 1 1

10. (15500)
    6786
    + 8595
    15381
    1 1 1

11. (10000)
    3642
    + 6272
    9914
    1

12. (12500)
    8872
    + 3569
    12441
    1 1 1

13. (15500)
    7535
    + 8169
    15704
    1 1

14. (11000)
    1368
    + 9453
    10821
    1 1

15. (12000)
    6768
    + 5387
    12155
    1 1 1

16. (10000)
    4934
    + 4945
    9879
    1

17. $\widehat{11000}$
3654
+ 7268
10922
$\overline{11}$

Explore Largest total = 16 173;
Smallest = 3825;
Largest even total = 16 146;
Smallest even total = 3834

Page 56
Adding

Estimates may vary.

1. $\widehat{10000}$
4683
742
3604
+ 28
9057
$\overline{211}$

2. $\widehat{4000}$
3568
47
+ 362
3977
$\overline{11}$

3. $\widehat{3500}$
1462
556
98
+ 1134
3250
$\overline{122}$

4. $\widehat{4000}$
2673
843
62
+ 359
3937
$\overline{121}$

5. $\widehat{8000}$
6437
362
12
+ 1794
8605
$\overline{121}$

6. $\widehat{10000}$
38
691
3742
+ 6438
10909
$\overline{121}$

7. Answers may vary.

Page 57
Adding

Estimates may vary.

1. $\widehat{15000}$
5436
9257
947
+ 368
16008
$\overline{222}$

2. $\widehat{16000}$
4169
597
6772
+ 4434
15972
$\overline{122}$

3. $\widehat{26000}$
8530
5540
3790
+ 7230
25090
$\overline{21}$

4. $\widehat{14000}$
2111
5414
768
+ 5602
13895
$\overline{\text{1 1}}$

5. $\widehat{12000}$
6663
1544
1555
+ 715
10477
$\overline{\text{2 1 1}}$

Explore Digital root of 3684 = 3; digital root of 5438 = 2. Digital root of 3684 + 5438 = 9122 = 5. The digital roots add to give the digital root of the answer to the original addition.

Page 58
Square numbers

1. $4 \times 4 = 16$
2. $5 \times 5 = 25$
3. $7 \times 7 = 49$
4. $3 \times 3 = 9$
5. $8 \times 8 = 64$
6. $6 \times 6 = 36$
7. $4^2 = 16$
8. $9^2 = 81$
9. $3^2 = 9$
10. $8^2 = 64$
11. $10^2 = 100$
12. $1^2 = 1$
13. $6^2 = 36$
14. $5^2 = 25$
15. $2^2 = 4$
16. $7^2 = 49$
17. $20^2 = 400$
18. $30^2 = 900$
19. 36
20. 49

21. 49
22. 9
23. 16
24. 36
25. 64
26. 81
27. 100
28. 81
29. 81
30. 100
Owl 121, 144, 169, or 196 holes.

Page 59
Square numbers

1. $7^2 = 49$
2. $2^2 = 4$
3. $10^2 = 100$
4. $3^2 = 9$
5. $8^2 = 64$
6. $1^2 = 1$
7. $9^2 = 81$
8. $5^2 = 25$
9. $6^2 = 36$
10.

Number	Square Number
10	100
20	400
30	900
40	1600
50	2500
60	3600
70	4900
80	6400
90	8100
100	10 000

11.

Number	Square Number
100	10 000
200	40 000
300	90 000
400	160 000
500	250 000
600	360 000
700	490 000
800	640 000
900	810 000
1000	1 000 000

Estimates for questions 12–19 may vary.
12. between 400 and 900, therefore 650
13. between 100 and 400, therefore 250
14. between 6400 and 8100, therefore 7250
15. between 490 000 and 640 000, therefore 565 000
16. between 360 000 and 490 000, therefore 425 000
17. between 90 000 and 160 000, therefore 125 000
18. between 8100 and 10 000, therefore 9050
19. between 10 000 and 40 000, therefore 25 000
Owl No. The only digits square numbers end on are 1, 4, 5, 6, 9 and 0.

Page 60
Square numbers

1. 30 mm
2. 60 mm
3. 20 mm
4. 50 mm
5. 80 mm
6. 40 mm

7.

10^2	20^2	30^2	40^2	50^2	60^2	70^2	80^2	90^2	100^2
100	400	900	1600	2500	3600	4900	6400	8100	10 000

Estimates for questions 8–5 may vary.
They should lie somewhere between:
8. 100–400
9. 900–1600
10. 8100–10 000
11. 400–900
12. 1600–2500
13. 4900–6400
14. 100–400
15. 8100–10 000
Exact answers:
8. 196
9. 1089
10. 8281
11. 529
12. 2401
13. 6084
14. 324
15. 9409
Owl
1. 900 cm²
2. 3600 cm²
3. 400 cm²
4. 2500 cm²
5. 6400 cm²
6. 1600 cm²
Explore $15^2 = 225$, $25^2 = 625$, $35^2 = 1225$, $45^2 = 2025$… They go up each time by a 200 more than the amount they increased the last time, i.e. the steps sizes above go 400, 600, 800, etc.

Page 61
Square numbers

1. $8^2 = 64$
2. $14^2 = 196$
3. $25^2 = 625$
4. $17^2 = 289$
5. $21^2 = 441$

6. $32^2 = 1024$
7. $19^2 = 361$
8. $41^2 = 1681$
9. $53^2 = 2809$
10. 9 and 16
11. 60
12. 16 and 25 or 25 and 9
13. 500
14. 70
15. 25 or 40 or 60 or 75

Explore Answers may vary.

Page 62
Sequences

1. 49, 56, 63, 70
2. 36, 30, 24, 18
3. 63, 72, 81, 90
4. 90, 75, 60, 45
5. 250, 275, 300, 325
6. 450, 525, 600, 675
7. 1400, 1250, 1100, 950
8. 625, 750, 875, 1000

Explore Fibonacci sequence: the rule is adding the previous two digits.

9. 76
10. 131
11. 191
12. 118
13. 13
14. 419

Page 63
Decimal and fraction sequences

1. 4, 4·5, 5, 5·5, 6
2. 0·8, 0·9, 1, 1·1
3. 1·9, 2·1, 2·3, 2·5
4. 2·5, 2·75, 3, 3·25
5. 1·8, 2·2, 2·6, 3
6. 9, 10·5, 12, 13·5
7. 4·8, 5, 5·2, 5·4
8. 20, 22·5, 25, 27·5
9. 8, 8·75, 9·5, 10·25
10. 10, 12·3, 14·6, 16·9

11. $3\frac{1}{3}$, 4
12. $3\frac{3}{4}$, $4\frac{1}{4}$
13. $4\frac{1}{3}$, 5
14. $2\frac{1}{4}$, $3\frac{3}{4}$, $5\frac{1}{4}$

Owl Answers may vary.

Page 64
Triangular numbers

1. 1
2. 3
3. 6
4. 10
5. 21
6. 45
7. 15
8. 21
9. 45
10. 36
11. 55
12. 120

Owl They are square numbers.

Explore Answers may vary. The difference is always the same as the middle number, e.g. the difference between 6^2 (36) and 3 × 10 (30) is 6. With the consecutive triangular numbers 10, 15 and 21, for example, the difference between 15^2 (225) and 10 × 21 (210) is 15.

Block E2
Page 65
Multiplying

1.
~~1500~~
528
× 3
24
60
1500
1584

2. (2000)
```
   464
 ×   4
    16
   240
  1600
  1856
```

3. (4200)
```
   732
 ×   6
    12
   180
  4200
  4392
```

4. (1200)
```
   326
 ×   4
    24
    80
  1200
  1304
```

5. (1500)
```
   458
 ×   3
    24
   150
  1200
  1374
```

6. (4200)
```
   724
 ×   6
    24
   120
  4200
  4344
```

7. (2400)
```
   562
 ×   4
     8
   240
  2000
  2248
```

8. (2000)
```
   395
 ×   5
    25
   450
  1500
  1975
```

9. (2400)
```
   643
 ×   4
    12
   160
  2400
  2572
```

10. (3500)
```
   527
 ×   7
    49
   140
  3500
  3689
```

11. (2100)
```
   741
 ×   3
     3
   120
  2100
  2223
```

12. 1704 boxes
13. 592 boxes
14. 1104 boxes
15. 1300 boxes
16. 2168 boxes
17. 1764 boxes

Owl
12. £106·50
13. £37
14. £69
15. £81·25
16. £135·50
17. £110·25

Page 66

Multiplying

1. (24000)
      4312
   ×   6
         12
         60
       1800
      24000
      25872

2. (20000)
      5473
   ×   4
         12
        280
       1600
      20000
      21892

3. (20000)
      3627
   ×   5
         35
        100
       3000
      15000
      18135

4. (16000)
      4263
   ×   4
         12
        240
        800
      16000
      17052

5. (16000)
      3725
   ×   4
         20
         80
       2800
      12000
      14900

6. (12000)
      4368
   ×   3
         24
        180
        900
      12000
      13104

7. (30000)
      5274
   ×   6
         24
        420
       1200
      30000
      31644

8. (12000)
      3429
   ×   4
         36
         80
       1600
      12000
      13716

9. (7000)
      1438
   ×   7
         56
        210
       2800
       7000
      10066

10. (24000)
      2546
   ×   8
         48
        320
       4000
      16000
      20368

11. $\widehat{15000}$
3472
× 5
10
350
2000
15000
17360

12. $\widehat{24000}$
4135
× 6
30
180
600
24000
24810

13. 8292 cupcakes sold
14. 12 282 cupcakes sold
15. 11 658 cupcakes sold
16. 13 584 cupcakes sold
17. 10 698 cupcakes sold
18. 8712 cupcakes sold
19. 11 244 cupcakes sold
20. 12 834 cupcakes sold
21. 7656 cupcakes sold
Owl 1 000 000 ÷ 2500 = 400. It would take approximately 400 months to sell a million boxes.

Page 67
Multiplying

Predictions may vary.

1. $\widehat{9000}$
4537
× 2
9074

2. $\widehat{14800}$
3679
× 4
14716

3. $\widehat{10000}$
2531
× 4
10124

4. $\widehat{10200}$
1748
× 6
10488

5. $\widehat{11200}$
1435
× 8
11480

6. $\widehat{9500}$
1897
× 5
9485

7. $\widehat{9800}$
1362
× 7
9534

8. $\widehat{10400}$
2638
× 4
10552

9. $\widehat{9600}$
1234
× 8
9872

Explore Answers may vary.

Page 68
Multiplying

1. $\widehat{1568}$
× 4
6272

2. $\widehat{3428}$
× 3
10284

3. (5976)
     × 6
     ‾‾‾‾‾‾
     35856

4. (5728)
     × 5
     ‾‾‾‾‾‾
     28640

5. (3924)
     × 8
     ‾‾‾‾‾‾
     31392

6. (1645)
     × 7
     ‾‾‾‾‾‾
     11515

7. 4732 × £8 = £37 856
     £2144 less than £40 000

8. 2768 × 6 = 16 608 miles
     It can sail 13 392 more miles.

9. 4 × £4286 = £17 144
     3 × £2143 = £6429
     £17 144 + £6429 = £23 573

10. 8692 × 5 = 43 460p = £434·60
     8692 × 8 = 69 536p = £695·36
     They would have collected £260·76
     more if everyone had given 8p
     instead of 5p.

Owl Answers may vary.

Page 69   *Page 23.*

Fractions of amounts

1. $\frac{1}{4}$ of 8 = 2
     $\frac{3}{4}$ of 8 = 6
2. $\frac{1}{3}$ of 6 = 2
     $\frac{2}{3}$ of 6 = 4
3. $\frac{1}{5}$ of 10 = 2
     $\frac{3}{5}$ of 10 = 6
4. $\frac{1}{8}$ of 16 = 2
     $\frac{5}{8}$ of 16 = 10

5. $\frac{1}{6}$ of 12 = 2
     $\frac{5}{6}$ of 12 = 10
6. $\frac{1}{10}$ of 100 = 10
     $\frac{3}{10}$ of 100 = 30
7. $\frac{1}{10}$ of £70 = £7; $\frac{3}{10}$ of £70 = £21
8. $\frac{1}{5}$ of 15 cm = 3 cm; $\frac{2}{5}$ of 15 cm = 6 cm
9. $\frac{1}{4}$ of 32 kg = 8 kg; $\frac{3}{4}$ of 32 kg = 24 kg
10. $\frac{1}{8}$ of 40 ml = 5 ml; $\frac{7}{8}$ of 40 ml = 35 ml
11. $\frac{1}{100}$ of 700 km = 7 km;
     $\frac{8}{100}$ of 700 km = 56 km

Owl Answers may vary.

Page 70   *Page 24*

Fractions of amounts

1. $\frac{1}{100}$ of 400 g = 4 g
     (a) $\frac{7}{100}$ of 400 g = 28 g
     (b) $\frac{18}{100}$ of 400 g = 72 g
     (c) $\frac{51}{100}$ of 400 g = 204 g
     (d) $\frac{3}{10}$ of 400 g = 120 g
     (e) $\frac{7}{10}$ of 400 g = 280 g
     (f) $\frac{9}{10}$ of 400 g = 360 g
2. $\frac{1}{100}$ of 600 g = 6 g
     (a) $\frac{9}{100}$ of 600 g = 54 g
     (b) $\frac{11}{100}$ of 600 g = 66 g
     (c) $\frac{21}{100}$ of 600 g = 126 g
     (d) $\frac{4}{10}$ of 600 g = 240 g
     (e) $\frac{9}{10}$ of 600 g = 540 g
     (f) $\frac{6}{10}$ of 600 g = 360 g
3. $\frac{1}{100}$ of 1 kg = 10 g
     (a) $\frac{3}{100}$ of 1 kg = 30 g
     (b) $\frac{28}{100}$ of 1 kg = 280 g
     (c) $\frac{47}{100}$ of 1 kg = 470 g
     (d) $\frac{7}{10}$ of 1 kg = 700 g
     (e) $\frac{3}{10}$ of 1 kg = 300 g
     (f) $\frac{8}{10}$ of 1 kg = 800 g

4.

×	20	60	30	70
$\frac{1}{2}$	10	30	15	35
$\frac{3}{5}$	12	36	18	42
$\frac{3}{10}$	6	18	9	21

5.

×	40	80	130	420
$\frac{7}{10}$	28	56	91	294
$\frac{2}{5}$	16	32	52	168
$\frac{1}{4}$	10	20	32·5	105

6.

×	200	600	500	900
$\frac{1}{100}$	2	6	5	9
$\frac{4}{5}$	160	480	400	720
$\frac{21}{100}$	42	126	105	189

7.

×	300	700	1400	400
$\frac{33}{10}$	99	231	462	132
$\frac{9}{10}$	270	630	1260	360
$\frac{83}{100}$	249	581	1162	332

Owl Answers may vary.

Page 7I
Fractions of amounts

1. (a) $\frac{2}{3}$ of £48 = £32
   (b) $\frac{3}{4}$ of £48 = £36
   (c) $\frac{5}{6}$ of £48 = £40
   (d) $\frac{7}{12}$ of £48 = £28
   (e) $\frac{5}{8}$ of £48 = £30
   (f) $\frac{1}{24}$ of £48 = £2

2. (a) $\frac{3}{4}$ of £40 = £30
   (b) $\frac{4}{5}$ of £40 = £32
   (c) $\frac{7}{8}$ of £40 = £35
   (d) $\frac{11}{20}$ of £40 = £22
   (e) $\frac{9}{10}$ of £40 = £36
   (f) $\frac{3}{20}$ of £40 = £6

3. (a) $\frac{2}{3}$ of £120 = £80
   (b) $\frac{7}{12}$ of £120 = £70
   (c) $\frac{8}{15}$ of £120 = £64
   (d) $\frac{5}{6}$ of £120 = £100
   (e) $\frac{3}{5}$ of £120 = £72
   (f) $\frac{17}{20}$ of £120 = £102

4. $\frac{2}{3}$ of £6 = £4

5. $\frac{3}{4}$ of £48 = £36

6. $\frac{4}{5}$ of £30 = £24

7. $\frac{5}{6}$ of £24 = £20

8. $\frac{7}{12}$ of £24 = £14

9. $\frac{9}{10}$ of £120 = £108

10. $\frac{3}{8}$ of £48 = £18

11. $\frac{4}{7}$ of £28 = £16

12. $\frac{5}{9}$ of £72 = £40

13. $\frac{4}{11}$ of £88 = £32

14. $\frac{7}{20}$ of £120 = £42

15. $\frac{11}{25}$ of £250 = £110

Owl Answers may vary. Possible answers include A = 8, B = 9; A = 16, B = 18, etc.

Explore Answers may vary.

Page 72
Fractions of amounts

Guesses for answers 1–5 may vary.

1. (a) $\frac{1}{3}$ of 60 = 20, $\frac{2}{3}$ of 60 = 40
   (b) $\frac{1}{4}$ of 80 = 20, $\frac{3}{4}$ of 80 = 60
   (c) $\frac{1}{5}$ of 50 = 10, $\frac{4}{5}$ of 50 = 40
   (d) $\frac{1}{7}$ of 70 = 10, $\frac{5}{7}$ of 70 = 50

2. (a) $\frac{1}{5}$ of 25 = 5, $\frac{3}{5}$ of 25 = 15
   (b) $\frac{1}{6}$ of 18 = 3, $\frac{5}{6}$ of 18 = 15
   (c) $\frac{1}{4}$ of 16 = 4, $\frac{3}{4}$ of 16 = 12
   (d) $\frac{1}{5}$ of 20 = 4, $\frac{3}{5}$ of 20 = 12

3. (a) $\frac{1}{9}$ of 36 = 4, $\frac{4}{9}$ of 36 = 16
   (b) $\frac{1}{7}$ of 49 = 7, $\frac{3}{7}$ of 49 = 21
   (c) $\frac{1}{5}$ of 35 = 7, $\frac{4}{5}$ of 35 = 28
   (d) $\frac{1}{3}$ of 27 = 9, $\frac{2}{3}$ of 27 = 18

Page 25

Page 26.

4. (a) $\frac{1}{10}$ of 90 = 9, $\frac{7}{10}$ of 90 = 63

    (b) $\frac{1}{100}$ of 700 = 7, $\frac{11}{100}$ of 700 = 77

    (c) $\frac{1}{50}$ of 400 = 8, $\frac{9}{50}$ of 400 = 72

    (d) $\frac{1}{25}$ of 250 = 10, $\frac{3}{25}$ of 250 = 30

5. (a) $\frac{1}{12}$ of 60 = 5, $\frac{5}{12}$ of 60 = 25

    (b) $\frac{1}{11}$ of 77 = 7, $\frac{7}{11}$ of 77 = 49

    (c) $\frac{1}{15}$ of 90 = 6, $\frac{8}{15}$ of 90 = 48

    (d) $\frac{1}{20}$ of 80 = 4, $\frac{9}{20}$ of 80 = 36

6. 10

7. 18

8. £2·60

Owl Answers may vary.

Page 73
Fractions and decimals

1. $\frac{1}{4} = \frac{25}{100}$
2. $\frac{2}{5}$ or $\frac{4}{10} = \frac{40}{100}$
3. $\frac{1}{5}$ or $\frac{2}{10} = \frac{20}{100}$
4. $\frac{9}{10} = \frac{90}{100}$
5. $\frac{3}{4} = \frac{75}{100}$
6. $\frac{7}{10} = \frac{70}{100}$
7. $\frac{3}{5}$ or $\frac{6}{10} = \frac{60}{100}$

As decimals:

1. 0·25
2. 0·4
3. 0·2
4. 0·9
5. 0·75
6. 0·7
7. 0·6
8. $\frac{8}{10} = 0·8$
9. $\frac{9}{10} = 0·9$
10. $\frac{21}{100} = 0·21$
11. $\frac{37}{100} = 0·37$
12. $\frac{86}{100} = 0·86$
13. $\frac{1}{100} = 0·01$
14. $\frac{7}{100} = 0·07$
15. $\frac{121}{100} = 1·21$
16. $0·9 = \frac{90}{100}$

17. $0·2 = \frac{20}{100}$
18. $0·35 = \frac{35}{100}$
19. $0·89 = \frac{89}{100}$
20. $0·60 = \frac{60}{100}$
21. $0·11 = \frac{11}{100}$
22. $1·23 = \frac{123}{100}$
23. $1·56 = \frac{156}{100}$

Owl Answers may vary.

Page 74
Fractions and decimals

1. (a) $\frac{7}{10} = 0·7$
    (b) $\frac{2}{10} = 0·2$
    (c) $\frac{47}{100} = 0·47$
    (d) $\frac{85}{100} = 0·85$
    (e) $\frac{5}{100} = 0·05$
    (f) $\frac{95}{100} = 0·95$
    (g) $\frac{35}{100} = 0·35$
    (h) $\frac{62}{100} = 0·62$

2. (a) $\frac{275}{100} = 2·75$
    (b) $\frac{250}{100} = 2·5$
    (c) $\frac{225}{100} = 2·25$
    (d) $\frac{294}{100} = 2·94$
    (e) $\frac{232}{100} = 2·32$
    (f) $\frac{206}{100} = 2·06$
    (g) $\frac{259}{100} = 2·59$
    (h) $\frac{240}{100} = 2·4$

3. $\frac{7}{10} > 0·69$
4. $0·4 > \frac{39}{100}$
5. $\frac{20}{100} = 0·2$
6. $0·13 < 0·2$
7. $\frac{80}{100} = 0·8$
8. $\frac{3}{5} > 0·06$
9. $0·58 < \frac{6}{10}$
10. $\frac{45}{100} > 0·44$
11. $\frac{25}{100} = 0·25$

12. $\frac{9}{100} < 0.9$

13. $0.04 < \frac{4}{10}$

14. $\frac{30}{100} = 0.3$

15. $0.62 = \frac{62}{100}$

16. $\frac{82}{100} > 0.7$

17. $0.74 < \frac{75}{100}$

Owl Answers may vary.

Page 75
Fractions and decimals

1. 0·45
2. 0·62
3. 0·47
4. 0·29
5. 2·04
6. 0·54
7. 0·598
8. 0·445
9. $\frac{21}{100}, \frac{1}{4}, 0.27, 0.4, \frac{3}{5}$
10. $\frac{7}{10}, 0.72, \frac{3}{4}, \frac{78}{100}, 0.8$
11. $\frac{4}{5}, 0.815, 0.82, \frac{85}{100}, \frac{9}{10}$
12. $\frac{13}{16}, 0.85, 0.855, \frac{86}{100}, \frac{7}{8}$
13. $0.5, \frac{13}{25}, 0.535, 0.55, \frac{9}{16}$
14. $1.7, 1.725, 1\frac{3}{4}, 1.82, \frac{15}{8}$
15. $\frac{9}{4}, 2.3, 2.35, 2\frac{1}{2}, 2.535$
16. $4\frac{1}{5}, 4.24, 4.275, 4.3, 4\frac{3}{8}$

Explore Answers may vary.

Page 76
Fractions and decimals

1. $\frac{4}{5} = 0.8$
2. $\frac{3}{8} = 0.375$
3. $\frac{13}{25} = 0.52$
4. $\frac{11}{20} = 0.55$
5. $\frac{6}{15} = 0.4$
6. $\frac{3}{20} = 0.15$
7. $\frac{5}{8} = 0.625$
8. $\frac{18}{50} = 0.36$

9. $\frac{7}{8} = 0.875$
10. $\frac{9}{15} = 0.6$
11. $\frac{21}{25} = 0.84$
12. $\frac{7}{16} = 0.4375$
13. $\frac{1}{3} = 0.3333$
14. $\frac{2}{7} = 0.2857$
15. $\frac{4}{9} = 0.4444$
16. $\frac{2}{3} = 0.6666$
17. $\frac{12}{20}$
18. $\frac{7}{4}$
19. $\frac{23}{5}$
20. $1\frac{7}{20}$

Explore Answers may vary.

Page 77
Tests for divisibility

1. A number is divisible by 3 if the digits of that number add up to a number that is divisible by 3.
2. A number is divisible by 6 if you can divide it by 2 and then the digits of the answer add up to a number that is divisible by 3.
3. A number is divisible by 9 if the digits of that number add up to a number that is divisible by 9.
4. Yes
5. No
6. Yes
7. No
8. No
9. Yes
10. No
11. Yes
12. No
13. Yes
14. No
15. No

Owl A number is divisible by 18 if you can divide it by 2 and then the digits of the answer add up to a number that is divisible by 9.

Page 78
Tests for divisibility

1. true
2. false
3. true
4. true
5. false
6. true
7. true
8. true
9. false
10. true
11. 96, 78, 372, 124, 56, 216, 192, 432, 1044
12. 96, 372, 124, 56, 216, 192, 432, 1044
13. 96, 56, 216, 192, 432
14. 96, 78, 372, 39, 216, 192, 432, 1044
15. 96, 78, 372, 216, 192, 432, 1044
16. 216, 432, 1044
17. none
18. 175
19. none
20. Yes
21. Yes
22. No
23. No
24. Yes
25. Yes
26. No
27. Yes
28. Yes
29. No
30. No
31. Yes
Owl Answers may vary.

Page 79
Tests for divisibility

1.

	2	3	4	5	6	8	9	10	25	50
140	✓		✓	✓				✓		
270	✓	✓		✓	✓		✓	✓		
3000	✓	✓	✓	✓	✓	✓		✓	✓	✓
85				✓						
76	✓		✓							
432	✓	✓	✓		✓	✓	✓			
175				✓					✓	
234	✓	✓			✓		✓			
875				✓					✓	
4134	✓	✓			✓					

2. 27
3. 36
4. 37
5. 56 (or 126, 196…)
6. 72
7. 69
Owl Answers may vary. 189 000 has ten ticks.

Page 80
Tests for divisibility

1. true
2. false
3. true
4. true
5. false
6. true
7. false
8. false
Explore Answers may vary. There is no divisibility test for 7.

Textbook 3

Block A3

Page 3
Negative numbers

1. a) $^-1$
    b) 3
    c) $^-4$
    d) 5
    e) $^-7$
    f) $^-13$
    g) $^-10$
    h) 1
    i) $^-14$
    j) $^-11$
    k) $^-3$
2. $^-14$, $^-13$, $^-11$, $^-10$, $^-7$, $^-4$, $^-3$, $^-1$, 1, 3, 5
3. $^-4 < 3$
4. $^-1 > ^-5$
5. $^-10 < 5$
6. $^-3 > ^-8$
7. $^-14 < ^-6$
8. $^-15 < 1$
9. $^-6 > ^-12$
10. $2 > ^-4$
11. $^-8 < 6$
12. $^-5 < ^-1$
13. $1 > ^-9$
14. $4 > ^-7$

Explore Difference between: $^-1$ and $^+1 = 2$; $^-2$ and $^+2 = 4$; $^-3$ and $^+3 = 6$; other answers may vary.

Page 4
Negative numbers

1. a) $^-3$
    b) $^-17$
    c) $^-12$
    d) $^-7$
    e) 3

f) $^-23$
g) 7
h) $^-15$
i) $^-26$
j) 0
k) $^-9$

2. $^-26$, $^-23$, $^-17$, $^-15$, $^-12$, $^-9$, $^-7$, $^-3$, 0, 3, 7
3. $^-5 < 6$
4. $^-2 > ^-3$
5. $^-4 < 1$
6. $^-1 > ^-10$
7. $^-3 > ^-8$
8. $^-5 < 4$
9. $^-9 > ^-15$
10. $2 > ^-3$
11. $^-7 < 6$
12. $5 > ^-3$
13. $1 > ^-2$
14. $6 > ^-4$
15. $^-8$, $^-4$, $^-2$, 3
16. $^-9$, $^-3$, 1, 0
17. $^-11$, $^-3$, 1, 3
18. $^-8$, $^-5$, 3, 6
19. $^-3$, $^-1$, 4, 9
20. $^-12$, $^-8$, 3, 11
Owl 100 weeks

Page 5
Negative numbers

1. $^-10°$, $^-1°$, $4°$
2. $^-6°$, $^-2°$, $0°$
3. $^-15°$, $^-10°$, $^-9°$
4. $^-8°$, $^-7°$, $6°$, $9°$
5. $^-7°$, $^-6°$, $^-1°$, $5°$, $9°$
6. $^-7°$, $4°$, $12°$
7. $^-8°$, $^-6°$, $4°$, $14°$
8. $^-8°$, $^-2°$, $0°$, $1°$, $9°$
9. $^-9°$, $^-7°$, $^-3°$, $5°$
10. $^-15°$, $^-8°$, $^-4°$, $10°$, $12°$
11. $^-9°$, $^-7°$, $6°$, $12°$

12. -8°, -6°, -1°, 3°, 5°
13. -1°
14. -14°
15. -6°
16. 0°
17. -10°
18. -18°
19. 3°
20. -5°
21. -20°
22. -8°
Owl Answers may vary.

Page 6
Negative numbers

1. up 3° = -2°, fall 2° = -4°,
   fall 12° = -16°, up 5° = -11°
2. up 6° = 2°, up 3° = 5°,
   fall 5° = 0°, up 1° = 1°
3. fall 4° = -7°, fall 5° = -12°,
   up 6° = -6°, fall 4° = -10°
4. up 8° = 24°, up 1° = 25°,
   fall 9°, = 16°, up 6° = 22°
5. fall 2° = -12°, fall 9° = -21°,
   fall 4° = -25°, fall 3° = -28°
6. up 3° = 12°, up 3° = 15°,
   up 5° = 20°, up 12° = 32°
7. fall 5° = -10°, fall 4° = -14°,
   fall 7° = -21°, up 8° = -13°
9. -£7
10. -£5
11. -£9
12. -£22
Owl Two: Oslo to Porto and Sofia to
   Porto

Page 7
Percentages

1. 10% of £14 = £1·40
2. 10% of £11 = £1·10
3. 10% of £12 = £1·20
4. 10% of £5 = 50p

5. 10% of £13 = £1·30
6. 10% of £8 = 80p
7. 10% of £9 = 90p
8. 10% of £15 = £1·50
20% of each price:
1. 20% of £14 = £2·80
2. 20% of £11 = £2·20
3. 20% of £12 = £2·40
4. 20% of £5 = £1·00
5. 20% of £13 = £2·60
6. 20% of £8 = £1·60
7. 20% of £9 = £1·80
8. 20% of £15 = £3·00
9. 10% of 14 = 1·4 m
   1·4 m = 140 cm
10. 10% of 7 = 0·7 m
   0·7 m = 70 cm
11. 10% of 6 = 0·6 m
   0·6 m = 60 cm
12. 10% of 4 = 0·4 m
   0·4 m = 40 cm
13. 10% of 750 = 75 cm
14. 10% of 8 = 0·8 m
   0·8 m = 80 cm
15. 10% of 3400 = 340 cm
16. 10% of 22 = 2·2 m
   2·2 m = 220 cm
17. 10% of 18 = 1·8 m
   1·8 m = 180 cm
18. 10% of 230 = 23 cm
19. 10% of 54 = 5·4 m
   5·4 m = 540 cm
20. 10% of 1200 = 120 cm
Owl Answers may vary.

Page 8
Percentages

1. $\frac{1}{2}$ = 50%
   $\frac{1}{4}$ = 25%
   $\frac{1}{5}$ = 20%
   $\frac{3}{4}$ = 75%
   $\frac{1}{100}$ = 1%
   $\frac{1}{10}$ = 10%
   $\frac{1}{8}$ = 12·5%

2. 10% of £12 = £1·20
30% of £12 = £3·60
3. 10% of £14 = £1·40
40% of £14 = £5·60
4. 10% of £15 = £1·50
30% of £15 = £4·50
5. 10% of £16 = £1·60
40% of £16 = £6·40
6. 10% of £27 = £2·70
20% of £27 = £5·40
7. 10% of £22 = £2·20
60% of £22 = £13·20
8. 10% of £19 = £1·90
30% of £19 = £5·70
9. 10% of £23 = £2·30
40% of £23 = £9·20
Owl 1% of 1 metre = 1 cm,
1% of 1 litre = 10 ml,
1% of 1 kg = 10 g.
Other answers may vary.

Page 9
Percentages

1.

$\frac{1}{2}$	$\frac{1}{4}$	$\frac{1}{10}$	$\frac{1}{5}$	$\frac{2}{5}$	$\frac{3}{10}$
50%	25%	10%	20%	40%	30%

$\frac{7}{10}$	$\frac{1}{100}$	$\frac{4}{5}$	$\frac{3}{5}$	$\frac{3}{4}$	$\frac{1}{8}$
70%	1%	80%	60%	75%	12·5%

2. 10% of £12 = £1·20
5% of £12 = £0·60
2·5% of £12 = £0·30
17·5% of £12 = £2·10
3. 10% of £18 = £1·80
5% of £18 = £0·90
2·5% of £18 = £0·45
17·5% of £18 = £3·15
4. 10% of £16 = £1·60
5% of £16 = £0·80
2·5% of £16 = £0·40
17·5% of £16 = £2·80
5. 10% of £14 = £1·40
5% of £14 = £0·70
2·5% of £14 = £0·35
17·5% of £14 = £2·45

6. 10% of £22 = £2·20
5% of £22 = £1·10
2·5% of £22 = £0·55
17·5% of £22 = £3·85
7. 10% of £26 = £2·60
5% of £26 = £1·30
2·5% of £26 = £0·65
17·5% of £26 = £4·55
8. 10% = 180
30% = 540
1% = 18
31% = 558
9. 10% = 140
20% = 280
1% = 14
21% = 294
10. 10% = 120
20% = 240
1% = 12
26% = 312
11. 10% = 80
50% = 400
1% = 8
52% = 416
12. 10% = 70
30% = 210
1% = 7
29% = 203
13. 10% = 110
40% = 440
1% = 11
43% = 473
14. 10% = 90
40% = 360
1% = 9
38% = 342
15. 10% = 60
40% = 240
1% = 6
46% = 276
Owl
2. 30p more
3. 45p more
4. 40p more
5. 35p more
6. 55p more
7. 65p more

Page 10

Percentages

1. $\frac{4}{20} = \frac{2}{10}$
$\frac{2}{10} = 20\%$

2. $\frac{7}{35} = \frac{1}{5}$
$\frac{1}{5} = 20\%$

3. $\frac{4}{16} = \frac{1}{4}$
$\frac{1}{4} = 25\%$

4. $\frac{10}{50} = \frac{1}{5}$
$\frac{1}{5} = 20\%$

5. $\frac{8}{16} = \frac{1}{2}$
$\frac{1}{2} = 50\%$

6. $\frac{12}{48} = \frac{1}{4}$
$\frac{1}{4} = 25\%$

7. $\frac{5}{15} = \frac{1}{3}$
$\frac{1}{3} = 33 \cdot 33\%$

8. $\frac{21}{28} = \frac{3}{4}$
$\frac{3}{4} = 75\%$

9. $\frac{6}{20} = \frac{3}{10}$
$\frac{3}{10} = 30\%$

10. $\frac{19}{25} = \frac{76}{100}$
$\frac{76}{100} = 76\%$

11. $\frac{45}{50} = \frac{9}{10}$
$\frac{9}{10} = 90\%$

12. $\frac{18}{27} = \frac{2}{3}$
$\frac{2}{3} = 66 \cdot 66\%$

13. £32

14. 150 kg

Explore Fractions $\frac{1}{2}, \frac{1}{3} \dots \frac{1}{10}$: 50%, 33·3%, 25%, 20%, 16·7%, 14·3%, 12·5%, 11·1%, 10%…

Page 11

Multiplying

1. 274×23

	200	70	4	
20	4000	1400	80	5480
3	600	210	12	+ 822
				6302

2. 156×32

	100	50	6	
30	3000	1500	180	4680
2	200	100	12	+ 312
				4992

3. 326×18

	300	20	6	
10	3000	200	60	3260
8	2400	160	48	+ 2608
				5868

4. 438×26

	400	30	8	
20	8000	600	160	8760
6	2400	180	48	+ 2628
				11 388

5. 267×34

	200	60	7	
30	6000	1800	210	8010
4	800	240	28	+ 1068
				9078

Written as a standard multiplication:

1.
```
    274
  × 23
  5480
+ 822
  6302
```

2.
```
    156
  × 32
  4680
+ 312
  4992
```

3.

$$326 \times 18$$

```
  326
×  18
──────
 3260
+2608
──────
 5868
```

4.

```
  438
×  26
──────
 8760
+2628
──────
11388
```

5.

```
  267
×  34
──────
 8010
+1068
──────
 9078
```

6. $213 \times 14 = 2982$
7. $652 \times 23 = 14\,996$
8. $821 \times 32 = 26\,272$
9. $734 \times 26 = 19\,084$
10. $513 \times 19 = 9747$
11. $525 \times 24 = 12\,600$

Owl Answers may vary. Rounding each distance to the nearest hundred miles we can say that, to cover 5000 miles takes approximately:

6. 25 trips
7. 7 trips
8. 6 trips
9. 7 trips
10. 10 trips
11. 10 trips

Page 12
Multiplying

Estimates for questions 1–18 may vary.

1. £5000

```
  238
×  24
   1
──────
 4760
+ 952
  13
──────
 5712
  11
```

2. £3000

```
  149
×  28
   1
──────
 2980
+1192
 37
──────
 4172
 11
```

3. £2500

```
  117
×  23
   1
──────
 2340
+ 351
   2
──────
 2691
```

4. £2000

```
  137
×  18
──────
 1370
+1096
 25
──────
 2466
  1
```

5. £5000

```
  246
×  25
   1
──────
 4920
+1230
 23
──────
 6150
  1
```

6. £6000

```
  324
×  19
──────
 3240
+2916
 23
──────
 6156
  1
```

7. 8000

```
  427
×  21
   1
──────
 8540
+ 427
──────
 8967
```

8. （9000）

316

× 32

1

9480

+ 632

1

10112

11

9. （8000）

235

× 43

1 2

9400

+ 705

1 1

10105

1

10. （25 000）

547

× 54

2 3

27350

+ 2188

1 2

29538

1

11. （6000）

189

× 26

1 1

3780

+ 1134

5 5

4914

1

12. （6000）

237

× 33

1 2

7110

+ 711

1 2

7821

13. （15 000）

347

× 48

1 2

13880

+ 2776

3 5

16656

1 1

14. （15 000）

526

× 29

1

10520

+ 4734

2 5

15254

1

15. （24 000）

637

× 36

1 2

19110

+ 3822

2 4

22932

1

16. （10 000）

483

× 23

1

9660

+ 1449

2

11109

1 1

17. （24 000）

615

× 44

2

24600

+ 2460

2

27060

1

18.
$\overline{8000}$
384
× 21
1

7680
+ 384

8064
11

Owl Answers may vary.

Page 13

Multiplying

1. Tim, Jack and Su Li
2. Jenny
3. Ranjit and Devi

Corrected answers:
524 × 18
9432
294 × 18
5292
436 × 27
11772
546 × 23
12558
463 × 34
15742
518 × 33
17094
356 × 42
14952

4. 2880 (2904 if it is a leap year)
5. 2952
6. 2928
7. 2928
8. 6901 m²
9. 7276 m²
10. 7314 m²

Owl Answers may vary.

Page 14

Multiplying

1. $\overline{6000}$
138
× 64
24

8280
+ 552
13

8832
1

2. $\overline{4500}$
154
× 32
11

4620
+ 308
1

4928

3. $\overline{8000}$
183
× 43
31

7320
+ 549
2

7869

4. $\overline{10\,000}$
247
× 48
12

9880
+ 1976
35

11856
11

5. $\overline{10\,000}$
221
× 54
1

11050
+ 884

11934
1

6. (6000)
$$109$$
$$\times \quad 58$$
$$ \quad 4$$
$$\overline{5450}$$
$$+ \quad 872$$
$$ 7$$
$$\overline{6322}$$
$$1\,1$$

7. (16 000)
$$237$$
$$\times \quad 82$$
$$ \quad 2\,5$$
$$\overline{18960}$$
$$+ \quad 474$$
$$ 1$$
$$\overline{19434}$$
$$1\,1$$

8. £14 778

9. 2376 miles

Explore 35 × 467 gives the smallest possible answer (16 345); 74 × 653 gives the largest possible answer (48 322)

Page 15

Multiplying decimals

1. $7 \times 4 \cdot 3$
(28)
$7 \times 4 \quad = 28$
$\underline{7 \times 0 \cdot 3 = 2 \cdot 1}$
$\underline{7 \times 4 \cdot 3 = 30 \cdot 1}$

2. $8 \times 5 \cdot 2$
(40)
$8 \times 5 \quad = 40$
$\underline{8 \times 0 \cdot 2 = 1 \cdot 6}$
$\underline{8 \times 4 \cdot 3 = 41 \cdot 6}$

3. $4 \times 3 \cdot 6$
(16)
$4 \times 3 \quad = 12$
$\underline{4 \times 0 \cdot 6 = 2 \cdot 4}$
$\underline{4 \times 3 \cdot 6 = 14 \cdot 4}$

4. $3 \times 5 \cdot 8$
(18)
$3 \times 5 \quad = 15$
$\underline{3 \times 0 \cdot 8 = 2 \cdot 4}$
$\underline{3 \times 5 \cdot 8 = 17 \cdot 4}$

5. $9 \times 6 \cdot 4$
(54)
$9 \times 6 \quad = 54$
$\underline{9 \times 0 \cdot 4 = 3 \cdot 6}$
$\underline{9 \times 6 \cdot 4 = 57 \cdot 6}$

6. $6 \times 7 \cdot 8$
(48)
$6 \times 7 \quad = 42$
$\underline{6 \times 0 \cdot 8 = 4 \cdot 8}$
$\underline{6 \times 7 \cdot 8 = 46 \cdot 8}$

7. $4 \times 2 \cdot 9$
(12)
$4 \times 2 \quad = 8$
$\underline{4 \times 0 \cdot 9 = 3 \cdot 6}$
$\underline{4 \times 2 \cdot 9 = 11 \cdot 6}$

8. $3 \times 7 \cdot 7$
(24)
$3 \times 7 \quad = 21$
$\underline{3 \times 0 \cdot 7 = 2 \cdot 1}$
$\underline{3 \times 7 \cdot 7 = 23 \cdot 1}$

9. $5 \times 4 \cdot 6$
(25)
$5 \times 4 \quad = 20$
$\underline{5 \times 0 \cdot 6 = 3}$
$\underline{5 \times 4 \cdot 6 = 23}$

10. $3 \times 6 \cdot 3$
(18)
$3 \times 6 \quad = 18$
$\underline{3 \times 0 \cdot 3 = 0 \cdot 9}$
$\underline{3 \times 6 \cdot 3 = 18 \cdot 9}$

11. $5 \times 2 \cdot 8$
(15)
$5 \times 2 \quad = 10$
$\underline{5 \times 0 \cdot 8 = 4}$
$\underline{5 \times 2 \cdot 8 = 14}$

12. $4 \times 5 \cdot 4$
$\qquad$ (20)
$\qquad$ $4 \times 5 \quad = 20$
$\qquad$ $4 \times 0 \cdot 4 = \quad 1 \cdot 6$
$\qquad$ $4 \times 5 \cdot 4 = 21 \cdot 6$

13. $3 \times 6 \cdot 6$
$\qquad$ (21)
$\qquad$ $3 \times 6 \quad = 18$
$\qquad$ $3 \times 0 \cdot 6 = \quad 1 \cdot 8$
$\qquad$ $3 \times 6 \cdot 6 = 19 \cdot 8$

14. $5 \times 3 \cdot 7$
$\qquad$ (20)
$\qquad$ $5 \times 3 \quad = 15$
$\qquad$ $5 \times 0 \cdot 7 = \quad 3 \cdot 5$
$\qquad$ $5 \times 3 \cdot 7 = 18 \cdot 5$

15. $4 \times 4 \cdot 3$
$\qquad$ (16)
$\qquad$ $4 \times 4 \quad = 16$
$\qquad$ $4 \times 0 \cdot 3 = \quad 1 \cdot 2$
$\qquad$ $4 \times 4 \cdot 3 = 17 \cdot 2$

16. $8 \times 2 \cdot 7$
$\qquad$ (24)
$\qquad$ $8 \times 2 \quad = 16$
$\qquad$ $8 \times 0 \cdot 7 = \quad 5 \cdot 6$
$\qquad$ $8 \times 2 \cdot 7 = 21 \cdot 6$

17. $4 \times 5 \cdot 6$
$\qquad$ (24)
$\qquad$ $4 \times 5 \quad = 20$
$\qquad$ $4 \times 0 \cdot 6 = \quad 2 \cdot 4$
$\qquad$ $4 \times 5 \cdot 6 = 22 \cdot 4$

18. $7 \times 9 \cdot 2$
$\qquad$ (63)
$\qquad$ $7 \times 9 \quad = 63$
$\qquad$ $7 \times 0 \cdot 2 = \quad 1 \cdot 4$
$\qquad$ $7 \times 9 \cdot 2 = 64 \cdot 4$

19. $5 \times 6 \cdot 4$
$\qquad$ (30)
$\qquad$ $5 \times 6 \quad = 30$
$\qquad$ $5 \times 0 \cdot 4 = \quad 2$
$\qquad$ $5 \times 6 \cdot 4 = 32$

20. $6 \times 9 \cdot 4$
$\qquad$ (54)
$\qquad$ $6 \times 9 \quad = 54$
$\qquad$ $6 \times 0 \cdot 4 = \quad 2 \cdot 4$
$\qquad$ $6 \times 9 \cdot 4 = 56 \cdot 4$

21. $3 \times 8 \cdot 7$
$\qquad$ (27)
$\qquad$ $3 \times 8 \quad = 24$
$\qquad$ $3 \times 0 \cdot 7 = \quad 2 \cdot 1$
$\qquad$ $3 \times 8 \cdot 7 = 26 \cdot 1$

22. $7 \times 1 \cdot 9$
$\qquad$ (14)
$\qquad$ $7 \times 1 \quad = \quad 7$
$\qquad$ $7 \times 0 \cdot 9 = \quad 6 \cdot 3$
$\qquad$ $7 \times 1 \cdot 9 = 13 \cdot 3$

23. $6 \times 4 \cdot 7$
$\qquad$ (30)
$\qquad$ $6 \times 4 \quad = 24$
$\qquad$ $6 \times 0 \cdot 7 = \quad 4 \cdot 2$
$\qquad$ $6 \times 4 \cdot 7 = 28 \cdot 2$

24. $4 \times 7 \cdot 3$
$\qquad$ (28)
$\qquad$ $4 \times 7 \quad = 28$
$\qquad$ $4 \times 0 \cdot 3 = \quad 1 \cdot 2$
$\qquad$ $4 \times 7 \cdot 3 = 29 \cdot 2$

Owl Answers may vary.

Page 16

Multiplying decimals

1. $3 \times £4 \cdot 56$
$\qquad$ (£15)
$\qquad$ $3 \times £4 \cdot 00 = £12 \cdot 00$
$\qquad$ $3 \times £0 \cdot 50 = £ \; 1 \cdot 50$
$\qquad$ $3 \times £0 \cdot 06 = £ \; 0 \cdot 18$
$\qquad$ $3 \times £4 \cdot 56 = £13 \cdot 68$

2. $4 \times £3 \cdot 68$
$\qquad$ (£16)
$\qquad$ $4 \times £3 \cdot 00 = £12 \cdot 00$
$\qquad$ $4 \times £0 \cdot 60 = £ \; 2 \cdot 40$
$\qquad$ $4 \times £0 \cdot 08 = £ \; 0 \cdot 32$
$\qquad$ $4 \times £3 \cdot 68 = £14 \cdot 72$

3. $5 \times £5.74$
($£30$)
$5 \times £5.00 = £25.00$
$5 \times £0.70 = £\ 3.50$
$5 \times £0.04 = £\ 0.20$
$5 \times £5.74 = £28.70$

4. $8 \times £8.72$
($£72$)
$8 \times £8.00 = £64.00$
$8 \times £0.70 = £\ 5.60$
$8 \times £0.02 = £\ 0.16$
$8 \times £8.72 = £69.76$

5. $3 \times £2.75$
($£9$)
$3 \times £2.00 = £6.00$
$3 \times £0.70 = £2.10$
$3 \times £0.05 = £0.15$
$3 \times £2.75 = £8.25$

6. $6 \times £7.85$
($£48$)
$6 \times £7.00 = £42.00$
$6 \times £0.80 = £\ 4.80$
$6 \times £0.05 = £\ 0.30$
$6 \times £7.85 = £47.10$

7. $8 \times £1.98$
($£16$)
$8 \times £1.00 = £\ 8.00$
$8 \times £0.90 = £\ 7.20$
$8 \times £0.08 = £\ 0.64$
$8 \times £1.98 = £15.84$

8. $(4 \times £1.98) + (4 \times £4.56)$
($£8 + £20 = £28$)
$4 \times £1.00 = £4.00$
$4 \times £0.90 = £3.60$
$4 \times £0.08 = £0.32$
$4 \times £1.98 = £7.92$

$4 \times £4.00 = £16.00$
$4 \times £0.50 = £\ 2.00$
$4 \times £0.06 = £\ 0.24$
$4 \times £4.56 = £18.24$
$(4 \times £1.98) + (4 \times £4.56)$
$= £7.92 + £18.24 = £26.16$

9. $4 \times £6.93$
($£28$)
$4 \times £6.00 = £24.00$
$4 \times £0.90 = £\ 3.60$
$4 \times £0.03 = £\ 0.12$
$4 \times £6.93 = £27.72$

10. $(5 \times £2.75) + (3 \times £5.74)$
($£15 + £18 = £33$)
$5 \times £2.00 = £10.00$
$5 \times £0.70 = £\ 3.50$
$5 \times £0.05 = £\ 0.25$
$5 \times £2.75 = £13.75$

$3 \times £5.00 = £15.00$
$3 \times £0.70 = £\ 2.10$
$3 \times £0.04 = £\ 0.12$
$3 \times £5.74 = £17.22$
$(5 \times £2.75) + (3 \times £5.74)$
$= £13.75 + £17.22 = £30.97$

11. $3 \times 1.26 = 3.78$
12. $4 \times 2.57 = 10.28$
13. $5 \times 4.36 = 21.8$
14. $8 \times 7.42 = 59.36$
15. $9 \times 3.87 = 34.83$
16. $4 \times 8.64 = 34.56$
17. $7 \times 3.92 = 27.44$
18. $6 \times 4.38 = 26.28$
19. $9 \times 5.28 = 47.52$
Owl Answers may vary.

Page 17
Multiplying decimals

1. 5×4.32
(20)
$5 \times 4\ \ \ = 20$
$5 \times 0.3\ \ = \ \ 1.5$
$5 \times 0.02 = \ \ 0.10$
$5 \times 4.32 = 21.6$

2. 6×3.78
(24)
$6 \times 3\ \ \ = 18$
$6 \times 0.7\ \ = \ \ 4.2$
$6 \times 0.08 = \ \ 0.48$
$6 \times 3.78 = 22.68$

3. $2 \times 9 \cdot 41$

(18)

$2 \times 9 \quad = 18$
$2 \times 0 \cdot 4 \quad = \quad 0 \cdot 8$
$2 \times 0 \cdot 01 = \quad 0 \cdot 02$
$2 \times 9 \cdot 41 = 18 \cdot 82$

4. $3 \times 6 \cdot 75$

(21)

$3 \times 6 \quad = 18$
$3 \times 0 \cdot 7 \quad = \quad 2 \cdot 1$
$3 \times 0 \cdot 05 = \quad 0 \cdot 15$
$3 \times 6 \cdot 75 = 20 \cdot 25$

5. $4 \times 5 \cdot 23$

(20)

$4 \times 5 \quad = 20$
$4 \times 0 \cdot 2 \quad = \quad 0 \cdot 8$
$4 \times 0 \cdot 03 = \quad 0 \cdot 12$
$4 \times 5 \cdot 23 = 20 \cdot 92$

6. $7 \times 2 \cdot 85$

(21)

$7 \times 2 \quad = 14$
$7 \times 0 \cdot 8 \quad = \quad 5 \cdot 6$
$7 \times 0 \cdot 05 = \quad 0 \cdot 35$
$7 \times 2 \cdot 85 = 19 \cdot 95$

7. $8 \times 2 \cdot 23$

(16)

$8 \times 2 \quad = 16$
$8 \times 0 \cdot 2 \quad = \quad 1 \cdot 6$
$8 \times 0 \cdot 03 = \quad 0 \cdot 24$
$8 \times 2 \cdot 23 = 17 \cdot 84$

8. $9 \times 1 \cdot 84$

(18)

$9 \times 1 \quad = \quad 9$
$9 \times 0 \cdot 8 \quad = \quad 7 \cdot 2$
$9 \times 0 \cdot 04 = \quad 0 \cdot 36$
$9 \times 1 \cdot 84 = 16 \cdot 56$

9. $4 \times 4 \cdot 72$

(20)

$4 \times 4 \quad = 16$
$4 \times 0 \cdot 7 \quad = \quad 2 \cdot 8$
$4 \times 0 \cdot 02 = \quad 0 \cdot 08$
$4 \times 4 \cdot 72 = 18 \cdot 88$

Lucy's answer is nearest to 20; Ben's answer is second nearest

10. $4 \times 3 \cdot 24 = 12 \cdot 96$ cm
11. $5 \times 4 \cdot 56 = 22 \cdot 8$ cm
12. $8 \times 5 \cdot 73 = 45 \cdot 84$ cm
13. $3 \times 9 \cdot 28 = 27 \cdot 84$ cm
14. $6 \times 4 \cdot 47 = 26 \cdot 82$ cm
15. $9 \times 6 \cdot 83 = 61 \cdot 47$ cm
16. $6 \times 8 \cdot 67 = 52 \cdot 02$ cm
17. $8 \times 6 \cdot 84 = 54 \cdot 72$ cm
18. $5 \times 7 \cdot 68 = 38 \cdot 4$ cm
19. $4 \times 6 \cdot 37 = 25 \cdot 48$ cm
Owl triangle = 11·07 cm;
square = 14·76 cm;
pentagon = 18·45 cm;
hexagon = 22·14 cm;
heptagon = 25·83 cm;
octagon = 29·52 cm;
nonagon = 33·21 cm;
decagon = 36·9 cm

Page 18
Multiplying decimals

1. 4·72
2. 3·84
3. 4·32
4. 6·89
5. 5·76
6. 7·58
7. His fence is 5·12 m short; he needs to buy 3 more pieces
8. £12·48
9. £5·34

Explore Answers may vary.

Block B3
Page 19
Adding

1.   (7)

$$\begin{array}{r} 3 \cdot 32 \\ + 4 \cdot 18 \\ \hline 7 \cdot 50 \\ \hline \end{array}$$

2. ⬭11
$$\begin{array}{r} 6 \cdot 72 \\ +\ 3 \cdot 84 \\ \hline 10 \cdot 56 \\ \hline {\scriptstyle 1} \end{array}$$

3. ⬭8
$$\begin{array}{r} 4 \cdot 63 \\ +\ 2 \cdot 58 \\ \hline 7 \cdot 21 \\ \hline {\scriptstyle 1\ 1} \end{array}$$

4. ⬭8
$$\begin{array}{r} 5 \cdot 44 \\ +\ 2 \cdot 83 \\ \hline 8 \cdot 27 \\ \hline {\scriptstyle 1} \end{array}$$

5. ⬭6
$$\begin{array}{r} 3 \cdot 67 \\ +\ 2 \cdot 25 \\ \hline 5 \cdot 92 \\ \hline {\scriptstyle 1} \end{array}$$

6. ⬭8
$$\begin{array}{r} 4 \cdot 32 \\ +\ 3 \cdot 84 \\ \hline 8 \cdot 16 \\ \hline {\scriptstyle 1} \end{array}$$

7. ⬭7
$$\begin{array}{r} 6 \cdot 47 \\ +\ 1 \cdot 25 \\ \hline 7 \cdot 72 \\ \hline {\scriptstyle 1} \end{array}$$

8. ⬭10
$$\begin{array}{r} 4 \cdot 58 \\ +\ 5 \cdot 24 \\ \hline 9 \cdot 82 \\ \hline {\scriptstyle 1} \end{array}$$

9. ⬭7
$$\begin{array}{r} 4 \cdot 31 \\ +\ 2 \cdot 93 \\ \hline 7 \cdot 24 \\ \hline {\scriptstyle 1} \end{array}$$

10. ⬭6
$$\begin{array}{r} 5 \cdot 36 \\ +\ 1 \cdot 29 \\ \hline 6 \cdot 65 \\ \hline {\scriptstyle 1} \end{array}$$

11. ⬭7
$$\begin{array}{r} 3 \cdot 87 \\ +\ 2 \cdot 62 \\ \hline 6 \cdot 49 \\ \hline {\scriptstyle 1} \end{array}$$

12. 6·21 l
13. 7·51 l
14. 4·84 l
15. 8·88 l
16. 5·59 l
17. 8·34 l
Owl 10

Page 20
Adding

1. ⬭12
$$\begin{array}{r} 5 \cdot 06 \\ 3 \cdot 7 \\ +\ 2 \cdot 85 \\ \hline 11 \cdot 61 \\ \hline {\scriptstyle 1\ 1} \end{array}$$

2. ⬭11
$$\begin{array}{r} 6 \cdot 72 \\ +\ 3 \cdot 85 \\ \hline 10 \cdot 57 \\ \hline {\scriptstyle 1} \end{array}$$

3. ⬭8
$$\begin{array}{r} 4 \cdot 8 \\ 2 \cdot 05 \\ +\ 0 \cdot 87 \\ \hline 7 \cdot 72 \\ \hline {\scriptstyle 1\ 1} \end{array}$$

4. ⬭10
$$\begin{array}{r} 2 \cdot 68 \\ 4 \cdot 93 \\ +\ 1 \cdot 76 \\ \hline 9 \cdot 37 \\ \hline {\scriptstyle 2\ 1} \end{array}$$

5. ⬭10
$$\begin{array}{r} 5 \cdot 76 \\ +\ 3 \cdot 8 \\ \hline 9 \cdot 56 \\ \hline {\scriptstyle 1} \end{array}$$

6. (12)

5·36
4·4
+ 3·12
_____
12·88

7. (19)

3·57
8·2
+ 7·4
_____
19·17
1

8. (9)

6·18
+ 3·12
_____
9·30
1

9. (16)

5·72
6·84
+ 3·25
_____
15·81 kg
1 1

10. (21)

4·97
6·34
+ 5·12
_____
16·43 kg
1 1

11. (19)

6·79
4·38
+ 7·84
_____
19·01 kg
2 2

12. (14)

2·89
6·38
+ 4·64
_____
13·91 kg
1 2

13. (18)

5·64
7·92
+ 4·18
_____
17·74 kg
1 1

14. (15)

3·64
4·93
+ 5·78
_____
14·35 kg
2 1

15. (15)

3·84
6·47
+ 5·32
_____
15·63 kg
1 1

16. (10)

2·37
7·26
+ 1·19
_____
10·82 kg
2

Owl

9. 4·19 kg
10. 3·57 kg
11. 0·99 kg
12. 6·09 kg
13. 2·26 kg
14. 5·65 kg
15. 4·37 kg
16. 9·18 kg

Page 2I

Adding

1. £50·89
2. £78·47
3. £54·47
4. £74·89
5. £86·69
6. £88·31
7. £54·48
8. £57·97
9. 7·83 kg
10. pays £10·99; gets £9·01 change
11. £5·38
Owl Answers may vary.

Page 22

Adding

1. ⑧
   5·07
   0·65
   + 1·8
   ―――
   7·52
   1 1

2. ⑨
   3·75
   4·86
   + 0·07
   ―――
   8·68
   1 1

3. ⑫
   4·08
   3·9
   + 4·24
   ―――
   12·22
   1 1

4. ⑥
   1·4
   3·65
   + 0·795
   ―――
   5·845
   1 1

5. ⑬
   6·3
   4·098
   + 3·27
   ―――
   13·668
   1

6. ⑫
   6·09
   1·8
   + 4·067
   ―――
   11·957
   1

7. ⑮
   5·1
   3·7
   + 6·08
   ―――
   14·88

8. ⑬
   3·286
   7·07
   + 2·8
   ―――
   13·156
   1 1

9. false

10. false

11. false

Explore Answers may vary.

Page 23

Subtracting

Estimates may vary.

1. ⟨3000⟩
   $5\overset{2}{4}\overset{1}{3}2$
   − 2118
   ―――
   3314

2. ⟨4000⟩
   $4\overset{7}{8}26$
   − 1452
   ―――
   3374

3. ⟨2000⟩
   $6\overset{0}{1}\overset{1}{7}\overset{1}{2}8$
   − 4029
   ―――
   2099

4. ⟨3000⟩
   $\overset{6}{7}269$
   − 3542
   ―――
   3727

5. ⟨6000⟩
   $7\overset{5}{6}36$
   − 2172
   ―――
   5464

6. ⬭3000⬭

$$6\overset{7}{5}\overset{1}{\cancel{8}}3$$
$$-\ 4128$$
$$\overline{2455}$$

7. ⬭2000⬭

$$\overset{4}{\cancel{5}}\overset{1}{2}96$$
$$-\ 2734$$
$$\overline{2562}$$

8. ⬭1000⬭

$$4\overset{2}{8}\overset{1}{\cancel{3}}1$$
$$-3614$$
$$\overline{1217}$$

9. ⬭2000⬭

$$\overset{2}{\cancel{3}}\overset{1}{1}75$$
$$-\ 1432$$
$$\overline{1743}$$

10. ⬭3000⬭

$$56\overset{3}{\cancel{4}}\overset{1}{7}$$
$$-\ 2518$$
$$\overline{3129}$$

11. ⬭6000⬭

$$9\overset{5}{\cancel{6}}\overset{1}{2}8$$
$$-\ 4361$$
$$\overline{5267}$$

12. ⬭4000⬭

$$\overset{7}{\cancel{8}}\overset{1}{4}96$$
$$-\ 3753$$
$$\overline{4743}$$

13. ⬭5000⬭

$$7\overset{5}{\cancel{6}}\overset{1}{3}2$$
$$-\ 3271$$
$$\overline{4361}$$

14. ⬭7000⬭

$$94\overset{2}{\cancel{3}}\overset{1}{8}$$
$$-2219$$
$$\overline{7219}$$

15. ⬭2000⬭

$$\overset{4}{\cancel{5}}\overset{1}{2}96$$
$$-2534$$
$$\overline{2762}$$

16. ⬭4000⬭

$$8\overset{5}{\cancel{6}}\overset{1}{3}5$$
$$-5272$$
$$\overline{3363}$$

Owl 8765 – 1234 gives the largest possible answer of 7531

Page 24
Subtracting

Estimates may vary.

1. ⬭3000⬭

$$£4\overset{3}{\cancel{2}}\overset{1}{\cancel{8}}\overset{7}{4}$$
$$-£\ \ 768$$
$$\overline{£3516}$$

2. ⬭5000⬭

$$£5\overset{4}{\cancel{5}}\overset{1}{0}6$$
$$-£1285$$
$$\overline{£4221}$$

3. ⬭1000⬭

$$£4\overset{3}{\cancel{3}}\overset{1}{\cancel{8}}\overset{7}{1}$$
$$-£2816$$
$$\overline{£1565}$$

4. ⬭3000⬭

$$£3\overset{6}{\cancel{7}}\overset{1}{0}6$$
$$-£1375$$
$$\overline{£2331}$$

Textbook 3

5.   (2000)
    ² ⁴ ¹
  £3̷5̷27
  − £1643
  £1884

6.   (7000)
    ⁶ ³
  £7̷6̷4̷5
  − £ 837
  £6808

7.   (4000)
    ⁴ ³ ⁵
  £5̷4̷6̷3
  − £ 976
  £4487

8.   (4000)
    ⁸ ⁷
  £7̷9̷8̷5
  − £3697
  £4288

9.   (0)
    ⁵ ⁶
  £6̷4̷7̷3
  − £5728
  £ 745

10.   (4000)
    ⁴ ² ³
  £5̷3̷4̷2
  − £ 683
  £4659

11.   (4000)
    ⁷ ²
  £5̷8̷3̷5
  − £2348
  £3487

12.   (5000)
    ⁵ ³
  £6̷4̷37
  − £ 892
  £5545

13.   (50 000)
    ² ³
  53̷1̷4̷6
  − 2817
  50329

14.   (2000)
    ² ⁷
  3̷8̷8̷1
  − 1976
  1905

15.   (61 000)
    ³ ⁶
  64̷3̷7̷8
  − 2769
  61609

16.   (3000)
    ⁴ ³ ²
  5̷4̷3̷6
  − 1787
  3649

17.   (31 000)
    ² ¹ ⁵
  33̷2̷6̷5
  − 1678
  31587

18.   (3000)
    ⁵ ⁷
  6̷3̷8̷4
  − 2637
  3747

Owl Answers may vary.

Page 25
Subtracting

Estimates may vary.

1.   (2000)
    ² ⁴
  3̷5̷48
  − 1862
  1686

2.   (3000)
    ⁴ ⁰ ³
  5̷1̷4̷2
  − 1567
  3575

3. (2000)

$3\cancel{6}\cancel{4}\cancel{7}3$ (with small 5, 6 above)
$- 1625$
34848

4. (58 000)

$\cancel{6}17\cancel{8}6$ (with small 5, 7 above)
$- 4329$
57457

5. (6000)

$7\cancel{3}\cancel{2}4$ (with small 6, 2, 1 above)
$- 679$
6645

6. (34 000)

$5\cancel{8}4\cancel{3}5$ (with small 7, 2 above)
$- 23716$
34719

7. (2000)

$8\cancel{4}\cancel{3}1$ (with small 3, 2 above)
$- 6085$
2346

8. (12 000)

$2\cancel{6}\cancel{3}\cancel{4}5$ (with small 5, 2, 3 above)
$- 13867$
12478

Explore Answers may vary.

Page 26
Subtracting

1. 836 m
2. 27 m
3. 783 m
4. 305 m
5. 504 m
6. 1115 m

7. 810 m
8. 531 m
9. 332 m
10. 279 m
11. $46\,831 - 7994 = 38\,837$
12. $5218 - 3961 = 1257$
13. $7654 - 379 = 7275$
14. $64\,382 - 5317 = 59\,065$
15. $47\,932 - 8364 = 39\,568$
16. $6431 - 3786 = 2645$
17. $32\,465 - 6374 = 26\,091$
18. $4261 - 1794 = 2467$
19. $47\,653 - 24\,278 = 23\,375$
20. $22\,643 - 1875 = 20\,768$
21. $34\,652 - 26\,741 = 7911$
22. $18\,567 - 9379 = 9188$
Owl Answers may vary.

Page 27
Subtracting

Estimates may vary.

1. (1)

$\cancel{4}\cdot38$ (with small 3, 1 above)
$- 2\cdot55$
$1\cdot83$

2. (3)

$6\cdot\cancel{7}2$ (with small 6, 1 above)
$- 4\cdot38$
$2\cdot34$

3. (5)

$\cancel{6}\cdot52$ (with small 5, 1 above)
$- 1\cdot91$
$4\cdot61$

4. (4)

$7\cdot\cancel{6}4$ (with small 6, 1 above)
$- 3\cdot73$
$3\cdot91$

5. (6)

$$
\begin{array}{r}
8 \cdot \overset{5}{\cancel{6}}\overset{1}{2} \\
- 3 \cdot 49 \\
\hline
5 \cdot 13
\end{array}
$$

6. (1)

$$
\begin{array}{r}
\overset{5}{\cancel{6}} \cdot \overset{1}{4}3 \\
- 4 \cdot 82 \\
\hline
1 \cdot 61
\end{array}
$$

7. (5)

$$
\begin{array}{r}
6 \cdot \overset{2}{\cancel{3}}\overset{1}{3} \\
- 1 \cdot 28 \\
\hline
5 \cdot 05
\end{array}
$$

8. (3)

$$
\begin{array}{r}
\overset{5}{\cancel{6}} \cdot \overset{1}{3}8 \\
- 2 \cdot 74 \\
\hline
3 \cdot 64
\end{array}
$$

9. (3)

$$
\begin{array}{r}
\overset{6}{\cancel{7}} \cdot \overset{1}{2}4 \\
- 4 \cdot 33 \\
\hline
2 \cdot 91
\end{array}
$$

10. (4)

$$
\begin{array}{r}
5 \cdot \overset{5}{\cancel{6}}\overset{1}{2} \\
- 2 \cdot 37 \\
\hline
3 \cdot 25
\end{array}
$$

11. 0·75 m
12. 1·98 m
13. 1·95 m
14. 1·48 m
15. 1·23 m
16. 2·71 m
17. 1·22 m
18. 0·76 m
19. 0·47 m
20. 0·73 m
Owl 4·36 − 2·51 = 1·85

Page 28
Subtracting

Estimates may vary.

1. (£6)

$$
\begin{array}{r}
£1\overset{0}{\cancel{1}} \cdot \overset{1}{3}8 \\
- £\ 4 \cdot 86 \\
\hline
£\ 6 \cdot 52
\end{array}
$$

2. (£8)

$$
\begin{array}{r}
£1\overset{2}{\cancel{3}} \cdot \overset{1}{1}9 \\
- £\ 5 \cdot 37 \\
\hline
£\ 7 \cdot 82
\end{array}
$$

3. (£5)

$$
\begin{array}{r}
£1\overset{2}{\cancel{3}} \cdot \overset{1}{1}9 \\
- £\ 7 \cdot 92 \\
\hline
£\ 5 \cdot 27
\end{array}
$$

4. (£3)

$$
\begin{array}{r}
£1\overset{0}{\cancel{1}} \cdot \overset{1}{3}8 \\
- £\ 7 \cdot 92 \\
\hline
£\ 3 \cdot 46
\end{array}
$$

5. (£5)

$$
\begin{array}{r}
£1\overset{1}{\cancel{2}} \cdot \overset{1}{7}4 \\
- £\ 7 \cdot 92 \\
\hline
£\ 4 \cdot 82
\end{array}
$$

6. (£8)

$$
\begin{array}{r}
£1\overset{2}{\cancel{3}} \cdot \overset{1}{1}9 \\
- £\ 4 \cdot 86 \\
\hline
£\ 8 \cdot 33
\end{array}
$$

7. (£0)

$$
\begin{array}{r}
£\overset{4}{\cancel{5}} \cdot \overset{1}{3}7 \\
- £4 \cdot 86 \\
\hline
£0 \cdot 51
\end{array}
$$

8. (£3)

$$\begin{array}{r} {}^{8}\!\!{}_{1} \\ £7.\cancel{9}2 \\ -£4.86 \\ \hline £3.06 \end{array}$$

9. (£2)

$$\begin{array}{r} {}^{6}\!\!{}_{1} \\ £12.\cancel{7}4 \\ -£11.38 \\ \hline £\ 1.36 \end{array}$$

10. (£6)

$$\begin{array}{r} £11.38 \\ -£\ 5.37 \\ \hline £\ 6.01 \end{array}$$

11. £4.75

12. £8.87

13. £16.34

14. £10.53

15. £11.86

16. £5.79

Owl Answers may vary. Children should be able to get within 0.02 of 5, e.g. 8.61 − 3.59 = 5.02.

Page 29
Subtracting

Estimates may vary.

1. (77)

$$\begin{array}{r} {}^{7}{}^{15}\ {}^{16}\!\!{}_{1} \\ \cancel{8}\cancel{6}.7 0 \\ -\ 9.83 \\ \hline 76.87 \ \text{litres} \end{array}$$

2. (18)

$$\begin{array}{r} {}^{1}{}^{15}\ {}^{14}\!\!{}_{1} \\ \cancel{2}\cancel{6}.5 0 \\ -\ 8.75 \\ \hline 17.75 \ \text{litres} \end{array}$$

3. (50)

$$\begin{array}{r} {}^{6}\ {}^{12}\!\!{}_{1} \\ 57.\cancel{3} 0 \\ -\ 6.92 \\ \hline 50.38 \ \text{litres} \end{array}$$

4. (58)

$$\begin{array}{r} {}^{5}{}^{11}\ {}^{13}\!\!{}_{1} \\ \cancel{6}\cancel{2}.4 0 \\ -\ 3.71 \\ \hline 58.69 \ \text{litres} \end{array}$$

5. (67)

$$\begin{array}{r} {}^{6}{}^{13}\ {}^{14}\!\!{}_{1} \\ 7\cancel{4}.\cancel{5} 0 \\ -\ 7.84 \\ \hline 66.66 \ \text{litres} \end{array}$$

6. (36)

$$\begin{array}{r} {}^{3}{}^{15}\ {}^{12}\!\!{}_{1} \\ \cancel{4}\cancel{6}.\cancel{3} 0 \\ -\ 9.87 \\ \hline 36.43 \ \text{litres} \end{array}$$

7. (55)

$$\begin{array}{r} {}^{5}{}^{12}\ {}^{11}\!\!{}_{1} \\ \cancel{6}\cancel{3}.\cancel{2} 0 \\ -\ 7.64 \\ \hline 55.56 \ \text{litres} \end{array}$$

8. (46)

$$\begin{array}{r} {}^{4}{}^{14}\ {}^{13}\!\!{}_{1} \\ \cancel{5}\cancel{5}.\cancel{4} 0 \\ -\ 8.63 \\ \hline 46.77 \ \text{litres} \end{array}$$

9. £72.38

10. 64.45 m

11. 3.92 kg

Owl

$$\begin{array}{r} {}^{6}\!\!{}_{1} \\ 2.\cancel{7}4 \\ -\ 1.36 \\ \hline 1.38 \end{array}$$

$$\begin{array}{r} {}^{2} \\ \cancel{3}^{1}17 \\ -\ 1.54 \\ \hline 1.63 \end{array}$$

Page 30

Subtracting

Estimates may vary.

1. (69)

$7^1 6 \ ^1 4$
$\cancel{8}\cancel{7}\cdot\cancel{5}0$
$-18\cdot77$
$\overline{68\cdot73}$ kg

2. (68)

$8^1 5 \ ^1 2$
$\cancel{9}\cancel{6}\cdot\cancel{3}0$
$-27\cdot84$
$\overline{68\cdot46}$ kg

3. (33)

$6^1 1 \ ^1 3$
$\cancel{7}\cancel{2}\cdot\cancel{4}0$
$-38\cdot67$
$\overline{33\cdot73}$ kg

4. (64)

$7^1 3 \ ^1 1$
$\cancel{8}\cancel{4}\cdot\cancel{2}0$
$-19\cdot65$
$\overline{64\cdot55}$ kg

5. (35)

$5^1 2 \ ^1 1$
$\cancel{6}\cancel{3}\cdot\cancel{2}0$
$-27\cdot64$
$\overline{35\cdot56}$ kg

6. (36)

$7^1 2 \ ^1 5$
$\cancel{8}\cancel{3}\cdot\cancel{6}0$
$-47\cdot93$
$\overline{35\cdot67}$ kg

7. (59)

$8^1 2 \ ^1 6$
$\cancel{9}\cancel{3}\cdot\cancel{7}0$
$-34\cdot82$
$\overline{58\cdot88}$ kg

8. (57)

$6^1 3 \ ^1 2$
$\cancel{7}\cancel{4}\cdot\cancel{3}0$
$-16\cdot67$
$\overline{57\cdot63}$ kg

9. (36)

$7^1 1 \ ^1 3$
$\cancel{6}\cancel{2}\cdot\cancel{4}0$
$-25\cdot75$
$\overline{36\cdot65}$ kg

Owl Answers may vary.

Explore Answers may vary. You always get an answer which also has repeating digits.

Page 31

Capacity

1. 70 cl = 0·7 litres
2. 300 ml = 0·3 litres
3. 5 ml = 0·005 litres
4. 20 000 ml = 20 litres
5. 400 ml = 0·4 litres
6. 90 cl = 0·9 litres
7. 3000 ml = 3 litres
8. 4 ml = 0·004 litres
9. 1·5 l = 1500 ml
10. 0·55 l = 550 ml
11. 500 cl = 5000 ml
12. 2·5 l = 2500 ml
13. 0·65 l = 650 ml
14. 750 cl = 7500 ml
15. 4 l = 4000 ml
16. 1·75 l = 1750 ml
17. millilitres
18. litres (or gallons)
19. litres
20. millilitres
21. millilitres
22. litres (or pints)
23. millilitres
24. millilitres
25. litres
Owl 30 000

Page 32
Capacity

1. 40 litres
   = 8·8 gallons
2. 100 litres
   = 22 gallons
3. 18 litres
   = 4 gallons
4. 90 litres
   = 20 gallons
5. 45 litres
   = 10 gallons
6. 5 litres
   = 1·1 gallons
7. 20 litres
   = 4·4 gallons
8. 27 litres
   = 6 gallons
9. 30 litres
   = 6·6 gallons
10. 0·28 litres
11. 1 litre
12. 3·92 litres or 4 litres
13. 0·49 litres or 0·5 litres
Owl £5·31 per gallon (if 1 gallon = 4·5 litres). You would probably advertise the price per litre.

Page 33
Capacity

Answers to questions 1–9 may vary slightly.
1. 15 litres = 3·5 gallons
2. 2 gallons = 8·5 litres
3. 1·5 gallons = 6·3 litres
4. 4 gallons = 17·1 litres
5. 3·5 gallons = 15 litres
6. 5000 ml = 1·2 gallons
7. 10 l = 2·3 gallons
8. 2·5 gallons = 10·8 litres
9. 14 l = 3·25 gallons
Explore Answers may vary.

Block C3
Page 34
Probability

1. less than even
2. even chance
3. even chance
4. even chance
5. certain
6. less than even
7. even chance
8. more than even
9. even chance
10. less than even
Explore Answers may vary.

Page 35
Probability

1. one in ten $\frac{1}{10}$
2. one in ten $\frac{1}{10}$
3. six in ten $\frac{6}{10}$ or $\frac{3}{5}$
4. two in ten $\frac{2}{10}$ or $\frac{1}{5}$
5. two in ten $\frac{2}{10}$ or $\frac{1}{5}$
6. five in ten $\frac{5}{10}$ or $\frac{1}{2}$
7. none in ten 0
8. five in ten $\frac{5}{10}$ or $\frac{1}{2}$
9. three in ten $\frac{3}{10}$
10. four in ten $\frac{4}{10}$ or $\frac{2}{5}$
11. two in ten $\frac{2}{10}$ or $\frac{1}{5}$
12. four in ten $\frac{4}{10}$ or $\frac{2}{5}$
13. false
14. false
15. false
16. true
Owl Answers may vary.

Page 36
Probability

1. $\frac{3}{10}$
2. $\frac{1}{5}$
3. $\frac{1}{10}$

4. $\frac{2}{5}$

5. $\frac{7}{10}$

6. $\frac{2}{5}$

7. $\frac{1}{2}$

8. $\frac{9}{10}$

9. $\frac{7}{10}$

10. $\frac{3}{10}$

11. $\frac{0}{10}$

Owl Answers may vary.

Explore There is a $\frac{2}{5}$ chance of taking a prime number from cards 1–10; $\frac{2}{5}$ chance in cards 1–20; $\frac{1}{3}$ chance in cards 1–30; $\frac{3}{10}$ chance in cards 1–40; $\frac{3}{10}$ chance in cards 1–50; $\frac{17}{60}$ chance in cards 1–60; $\frac{19}{70}$ chance in cards 1–70; $\frac{11}{40}$ chance in cards 1–80; $\frac{4}{15}$ chance in cards 1–90; $\frac{1}{4}$ chance in cards 1–100.

Page 37
Probability

1. $\frac{1}{2}$

2. $\frac{1}{4}$

3. $\frac{1}{4}$

4. $\frac{1}{2}$

5. $\frac{2}{5}$

6. $\frac{1}{20}$

7. $\frac{1}{5}$

8. $\frac{1}{4}$

9. $\frac{1}{2}$

10. $\frac{1}{20}$

11. $\frac{1}{4}$

12. 0

13. $\frac{3}{4}$

14. $\frac{1}{5}$

15. $\frac{1}{40}$

16. $\frac{1}{2}$

17. $\frac{2}{5}$

18. 0

19. $\frac{1}{4}$

20. $\frac{1}{8}$

21. $\frac{1}{10}$

22. $\frac{1}{20}$

Explore Answers may vary.

Page 38
Pie charts

1. $\frac{1}{12}$

2. $\frac{1}{6}$

3. $\frac{1}{12}$

4. $\frac{1}{3}$

5. $\frac{1}{4}$

6. $\frac{5}{12}$

7. $\frac{3}{4}$

8. $\frac{5}{12}$

9. 20

10. 40

11. 30

12. 30

13. 30

14. 0

Owl Answers may vary. If 16 friends are surveyed, each wedge represents 2 people.

Page 39
Pie charts

1. pink

2. yellow

3. green

4. blue

5. 5

6. 2

7. 18

8. 2

9. 11

10. 4

Explore Answers may vary.

Page 40

Pie charts

1. $\frac{1}{4}$
2. $\frac{1}{6}$
3. $\frac{3}{4}$
4. $\frac{1}{6}$
5. $\frac{1}{4}$
6. $\frac{1}{3}$
7. 60
8. 30
9. 90
10. 270
11. 270
12. 60
13. Answers may vary.
Owl British = 36; Japanese = 24; USA = 12; Spanish = 12; Italian = 24; German = 12.

Page 41

Pie charts

1.

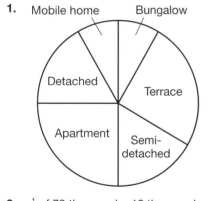

Mobile home Bungalow
Detached
Terrace
Apartment
Semi-detached

2. $\frac{1}{4}$ of 72 thousand = 18 thousand
3. $\frac{1}{12}$ of 144 thousand = 12 thousand
4. $\frac{1}{4}$ of 120 thousand = 30 thousand
5. $\frac{1}{12}$ of 108 thousand = 9 thousand
6. $\frac{1}{6}$ of 3600 thousand = 600 thousand
7. $\frac{1}{6}$ of 144 thousand = 24 thousand
8. $\frac{1}{12}$ of 72 thousand = 6 thousand
9. $\frac{1}{2}$ of 144 thousand = 72 thousand
10. $\frac{1}{3}$ of 120 thousand = 40 thousand
Owl Answers may vary.

Page 42

Perimeter

1. 22 + 27 = 49 cm
   49 × 2 = 98 cm
   0·98 m
2. 45 + 32 = 77 cm
   77 × 2 = 154 cm
   1·54 m
3. 19 + 46 = 65 cm
   65 × 2 = 130 cm
   1·30 m
4. 16 + 31 = 47 cm
   47 × 2 = 94 cm
   0·94 m
5. 32 + 18 = 50 cm
   50 × 2 = 100 cm
   1 m
6. 28 + 43 = 71 cm
   71 × 2 = 142 cm
   1·42 m
7. 39 + 17 = 56 cm
   56 × 2 = 112 cm
   1·12 m
8. 48 + 16 = 64 cm
   64 × 2 = 128 cm
   1·28 m
9. 33 + 22 = 55 cm
   55 × 2 = 110 cm
   1·10 m
10. 32 + 29 = 61 cm
    61 × 2 = 122 cm
    1·22 m
11. 41 + 27 = 68 cm
    68 × 2 = 136 cm
    1·36 m
12. 18 + 42 = 60 cm
    60 × 2 = 120 cm
    1·2 m
Explore Answers may vary.

Page 43

Perimeter

1. $3·5 + 4·8 = 8·3$
   $2 \times 8·3 = 16·6\,cm$
2. $4·2 + 5·6 = 9·8$
   $2 \times 9·8 = 19·6\,cm$
3. $5·1 + 6·4 = 11·5$
   $2 \times 11·5 = 23\,cm$
4. $4·3 + 7·5 = 11·8$
   $2 \times 11·8 = 23·6\,cm$
5. $3·5 + 4·2 = 7·7$
   $2 \times 7·7 = 15·4\,cm$
6. $2·2 + 3·6 = 5·8$
   $2 \times 5·8 = 11·6\,cm$
7. $3·6 + 5·1 = 8·7$
   $2 \times 8·7 = 17·4\,cm$
8. $4·4 + 7·3 = 11·7$
   $2 \times 11·7 = 23·4\,cm$
9. $16 + 8 = 24\,cm$
   $24 \times 2 = 48\,cm$
   $16 - 4 = 12\,cm$
   $8 - 4 = 4\,cm$
   $12 + 4 = 16\,cm$
   $16 \times 2 = 32\,cm$
   Difference = $16\,cm$
10. $18 + 13 = 31\,cm$
    $31 \times 2 = 62\,cm$
    $18 - 6 = 12\,cm$
    $13 - 6 = 7\,cm$
    $12 + 7 = 19\,cm$
    $19 \times 2 = 38\,cm$
    Difference = $24\,cm$
11. $12 + 8 = 20\,cm$
    $20 \times 2 = 40\,cm$
    $12 - 4 = 8\,cm$
    $8 - 4 = 4\,cm$
    $8 + 4 = 12\,cm$
    $12 \times 2 = 24\,cm$
    Difference = $16\,cm$

First Owl true
Second Owl Frame 9 has an area of $80\,cm^2$; frame 10 has an area of $24\,cm^2$; frame 11 has an area of $28\,cm^2$. Frame 9 is the biggest.

Page 44

Perimeter

1. $P = 14 + 12 + 9 + 5 + 5 + 7 = 52\,m$
2. $P = 3 + 16 + 3 + 5 + 4 + 6 + 4 + 5$
   $= 46\,m$
3. $P = 4 + 6 + 3 + 10 + 7 + 4 = 34\,m$
4. $P = 12 + 7 + 3 + 5 + 6 + 5 + 3 + 7$
   $= 48\,m$
5. $P = 13 + 2·3 + 9·3 + 3·7 + 3·7 + 6$
   $= 38\,m$
6. $P = 8 + 3·4 + 3 + 3·4 + 8 + 4·6 + 19$
   $+ 4·6 = 54\,m$
7. true
8. true
9. true
10. false
Owl Answers may vary.

Page 45

Perimeter

1. $14 + 12 = 26$
   $14 \div 2 = 7$
   $12 \div 2 = 6$
   $a = 3, b = 6, c = 4$
2. $16 + 8 = 24$
   $16 \div 2 = 8$
   $8 \div 2 = 4$
   $a = 5, b = 4, c = 2$
3. $12 + 8 = 20$
   $12 \div 2 = 6$
   $8 \div 2 = 4$
   $a = 2, b = 4, c = 1$
4. $18 + 10 = 28$
   $18 \div 2 = 9$
   $10 \div 2 = 5$
   $a = 4, b = 5, c = 2$
5. $12 + 12 = 24$
   $12 \div 2 = 6$
   $12 \div 2 = 6$
   $a = 4, b = 6, c = 5$
6. $14 + 12 = 26$
   $14 \div 2 = 7$
   $12 \div 2 = 6$
   $a = 4, b = 6, c = 3$

7. 6 + 12 = 18
6 ÷ 2 = 3
12 ÷ 2 = 6
a = 1, b = 6, c = 3
8. 10 + 12 = 22
10 ÷ 2 = 5
12 ÷ 2 = 6
a = 1, b = 6, c = 2

Explore The red shapes have the same perimeters and so do the blue shapes.

9. 9 m
10. true
11. 13·4 cm
12. A = 9 cm, B = 3 cm

Page 46

Time

1. 72
2. 300
3. 40
4. 28
5. 2
6. $\frac{1}{2}$
7. 156
8. 240
9. 600
10. 43 200
11. 52 weeks < 2 years
12. 360 minutes > 5 hours
13. 9 decades < 1 century
14. 48 hours > 1·9 days
15. 2 weeks < 1 month
16. 120 seconds > 1 minute
17. 1 fortnight < 20 days
18. 1 week > 161 hours
19. 80 days > 2 months
20. 180 seconds < 5 minutes
Owl Answers may vary. Estimates should fall between 400 × 75 and 350 × 75, i.e. between 30 000 and 26 250

Page 47

Time

Answers to questions 1–8 may vary.
9. false

10. false
11. false
12. true
13. true
14. false
Owl Estimates may vary. Should be 25 leap years in one century (one every four years).

Page 48

Time

1. 31
2. 30
3. 30
4. 31
5. 31
6. 31
7. 31
8. 31
9. 28 (29 in a leap year)
10. 30
11. 30
12. 31
13. 28 days
14. 43 days
15. 81 days (82 in a leap year)
16. 45 days
17. 143 days
18. 211 days (212 in a leap year)
19. 47 days
20. 59 days
21. 46 days (47 in a leap year)
22. 116 days
23. 86 days
24. 124 days
Owl Answers may vary.

Page 49

Time

1. 4:00 in Johannesburg
2. 6:00 in Rome
3. 11:00 in Denver
4. 10:00 in New York
5. 3:00 in Singapore
6. 1:00 in Rio de Janeiro

7. 5:00 in Singapore
8. 8:00 in Johannesburg
9. 17:00 in Rio de Janeiro
10. 17:00 in Singapore
11. 9:00 in New York
12. 14:00 in Rome
Owl Answers may vary.

Block D3

Page 50
Reflections

1.
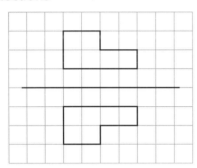

2.
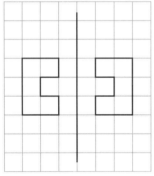

3.
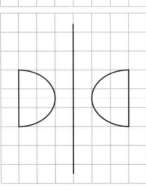

4.
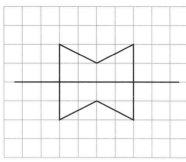

5.
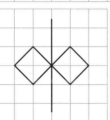

6.
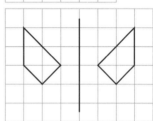

7.
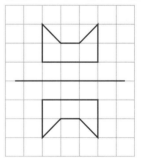

8.
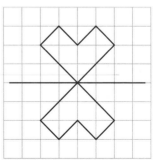

9.

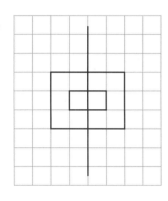

10.

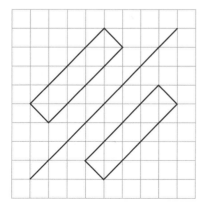

Owl Answers may vary.
Explore Answers may vary. Possible
answers include: A, H, M, O, W,
etc.

Page 51

Reflections

1.

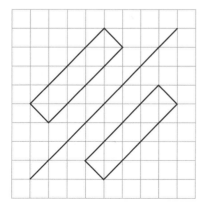

2.

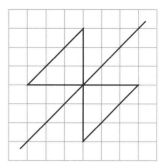

3.

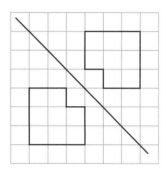

4.

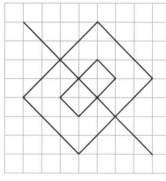

5.

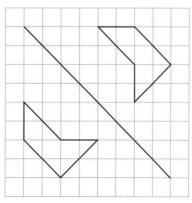

6.

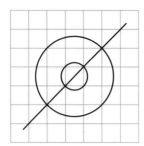

7.

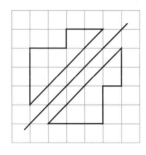

8.

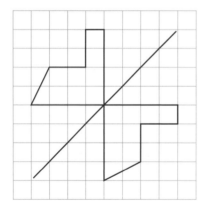

Explore Answers may vary. In a vertical mirror: A, H, I, M, O, T, U, V, W, X, Y (11); in a horizontal mirror: B, C, D, E, H, I, O, X (8).

Page 52
Reflections

1.

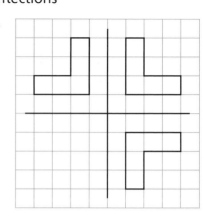

2.

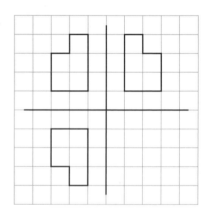

3.

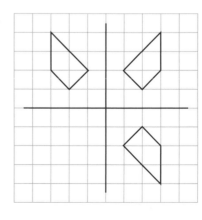

4.

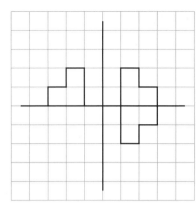

5.

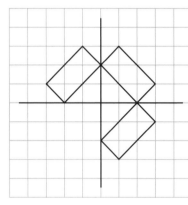

6.

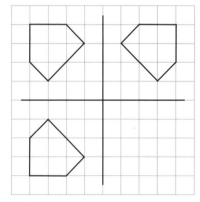

Explore Answers may vary.

Page 53
Reflections

1. (1, 1) (3, 2) (4, 4) (4, 1)
(⁻1, ⁻1) (⁻3, ⁻2) (⁻4, ⁻4) (⁻4, ⁻1)

2. (1, 2) (4, 4) (3, 1)
(⁻1, ⁻2) (⁻4, ⁻4) (⁻3, ⁻1)

3. (1, 1) (1, 4) (3, 3) (3, 1)
(⁻1, ⁻1) (⁻1, ⁻4) (⁻3, ⁻3) (⁻3, ⁻1)

4. (⁻1, 1) (⁻1, 5) (⁻2, 5) (⁻2, 2) (⁻3, 2)
(⁻3, 1)
(1, ⁻1) (1, ⁻5) (2, ⁻5) (2, ⁻2) (3, ⁻2)
(3, ⁻1)

5. (⁻1, ⁻1) (⁻1, ⁻4) (⁻2, ⁻4) (⁻2, ⁻3) (⁻3, ⁻3)
(⁻3, ⁻1)
(1, 1) (1, 4) (2, 4) (2, 3) (3, 3) (3, 1)

6. (1, ⁻1) (1, ⁻4) (2, ⁻2) (5, ⁻1)
(⁻1, 1) (⁻1, 4) (⁻2, 2) (⁻5, 1)

7. (⁻2, ⁻2) (⁻2, ⁻1) (⁻3, ⁻1) (⁻3, ⁻2) (⁻4, ⁻4)

8. (⁻3, ⁻1) (⁻4, ⁻2) (⁻1, ⁻2)

9. (⁻1, ⁻1) (⁻4, ⁻1) (⁻2, ⁻3) (⁻4, ⁻3)

10. (⁻2, ⁻2) (⁻3, ⁻2) (1, ⁻3) (⁻1, ⁻4) (⁻3, ⁻4)

Owl Answers may vary.

Page 54
Rotations

1.

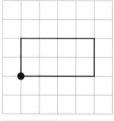

2.

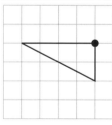

3.

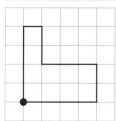

Textbook 3

4.

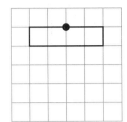

5.

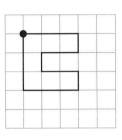

6.

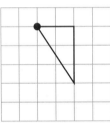

7.

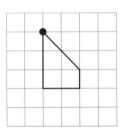

8.

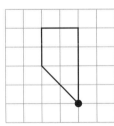

9. a
10. c
11. a
Owl Answers may vary.

Page 55

Rotations

1. a)

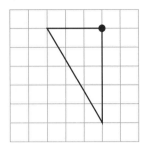

b)

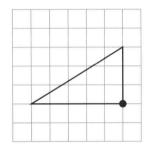

c)

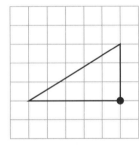

d)

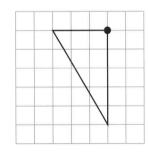

e)

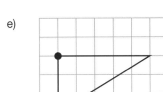

d)

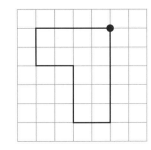

f)

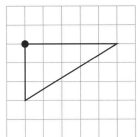

e)

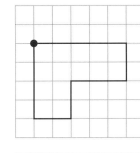

2. a)

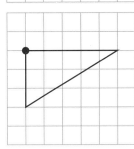

f)

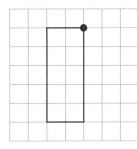

b)

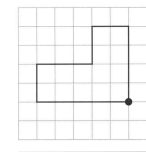

3. a)

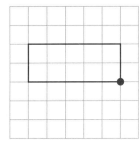

c)

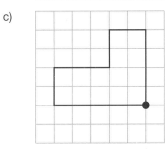

b)

c)

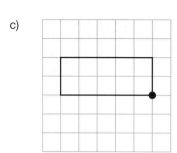

d)

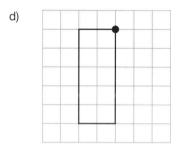

e)

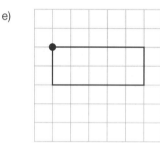

f)

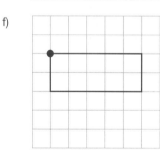

Explore After 90° clockwise: A (2, ⁻1);
B (1, ⁻1); C (1, ⁻2); After 180°
clockwise: A (⁻1, ⁻2); B (⁻1, ⁻1);
C (⁻2, ⁻1); After 270° clockwise:
A (⁻2, 1); B (⁻1, 1); C (⁻1, 2).
Answers for different shapes
may vary.

Page 56
Translations

1. (1, 1) (2, 3) (4, 3) (5, 1)
   (⁻2, 1) (⁻1, 3) (1, 3) (2, 1)
2. (1, 1) (1, 3) (5, 3) (5, 1)
   (1, ⁻1) (1, 1) (5, 1) (5, ⁻1)
3. (1, 1) (3, 3) (3, 1)
   (4, 1) (6, 3) (6, 1)
4. (1, 1) (1, 4) (3, 1)
   (⁻1, 1) (⁻1, 4) (1, 1)
5. (1, 3) (1, 4) (4, 4) (4, 3) (3, 3) (3, 1)
   (2, 1) (2, 3)
   (1, 6) (1, 7) (4, 7) (4, 6) (3, 6) (3, 4)
   (2, 4) (2, 6)
6. (1, 1) (1, 4) (2, 4) (2, 2) (4, 2) (4, 1)
   (⁻3, 1) (⁻3, 4) (⁻2, 4) (⁻2, 2) (0, 2) (0, 1)
7. (1, 3) (1, 4) (3, 4) (3, 1) (2, 1) (2, 3)
   (1, 0) (1, 1) (3, 1) (3, ⁻2) (2, ⁻2) (2, 0)
8. (1, 3) (2, 4) (3, 3) (2, 1)
   (3, 3) (4, 4) (5, 3) (4, 1)
9. (1, 1) (2, 3) (4, 3) (3, 1)
   (5, 1) (6, 3) (8, 3) (7, 1)
10. (1, 1) (1, 4) (4, 4) (2, 1)
    (1, 3) (1, 6) (4, 6) (2, 3)

Explore Answers may vary.

Page 57
Translations

1. a)

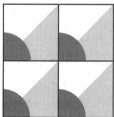

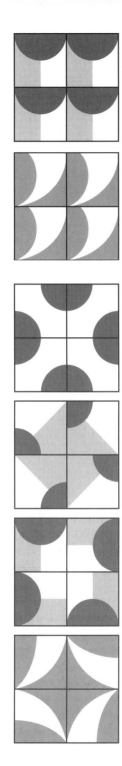

c)

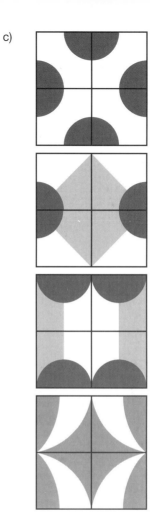

Explore Answers may vary.

Page 58
Dividing

Estimates for questions 1 – 7 may vary.

1.   (140)
    3)428
    − 300   100 × 3
    ─────
     128
    − 120   40 × 3
    ─────
       8
    −   6   2 × 3
    ─────
    = 142 r2

2. ⓘ(150)

```
4)573
- 400    100 × 4
  173
- 160    40 × 4
   13
-  12    3 × 4
= 143 r1
```

3. (160)

```
5)826
- 500    100 × 5
  326
- 300    60 × 5
   26
-  25    5 × 5
= 165 r1
```

4. (110)

```
4)464
- 400    100 × 4
   64
-  40    10 × 4
   24
-  24    6 × 4
= 116
```

5. (120)

```
5)575
- 500    100 × 5
   75
-  50    10 × 5
   25
-  25    5 × 5
= 115
```

6. (120)

```
3)369
- 300    100 × 3
   69
-  60    20 × 3
    9
-   9    3 × 3
= 123
```

7. (20)

```
5)105
- 100    20 × 5
    5
-   5    1 × 5
= 21
```

8. 144
9. 129 r1
10. 128 r3
11. 194 r4
12. 196
13. 181
14. 178
15. 164 r1
16. 156 r3
Owl   636 ÷ 4 = 159; 636 × 3 = 212;
each girl delivers 53 more papers.

Page 59

Dividing

Estimates for questions 1 – 8 may vary.

1. (140)

```
3)416
- 300    100 × 3
  116
-  90    30 × 3
   26
-  24    8 × 3
= 138 r2
```

2. (120)

```
5)627
- 500    100 × 5
  127
- 100    20 × 5
   27
-  25    5 × 5
= 125 r2
```

3. (180)

```
4)739
- 400    100 × 4
  339
- 300    75 × 4
   39
-  36    9 × 4
= 184 r3
```

4. $\boxed{240}$

```
  3)726
 - 600    200 × 3
   126
 - 120     40 × 3
     6
 -   6      2 × 3
 = 242
```

5. $\boxed{235}$

```
  4)943
 - 800    200 × 4
   143
 - 120     30 × 4
    23
 -  20      5 × 4
 = 235 r3
```

6. $\boxed{270}$

```
  3)827
 - 600    200 × 3
   227
 - 210     70 × 3
    17
 -  15      5 × 3
 = 275 r2
```

7. $\boxed{120}$

```
  5)623
 - 500    100 × 5
   123
 - 100     20 × 5
    23
 -  20      4 × 5
 = 124 r3
```

8. $\boxed{215}$

```
  4)862
 - 800    200 × 4
    62
 -  60     15 × 4
 = 215 r2
```

9. 148·25
10. 315·67
11. 154·8
12. 255·5
13. 145·17

14. 186
15. 282·67
16. 146
17. 123·83

Owl
9. 4447·5
10. 9470·1
11. 4644
12. 7665
13. 4355·1
14. 5580
15. 8480·1
16. 4380
17. 3714·9

Page 60

Dividing

Estimates for questions 1–12 may vary.

1. $\boxed{20}$

```
        24
  18)432
  - 360    20 × 18
     72
  -  72     4 × 18
```

2. $\boxed{30}$

```
        31
  14)434
  - 420    30 × 14
     14
  -  14     1 × 14
```

3. $\boxed{30}$

```
        28
  22)616
  - 440    20 × 22
    176
  - 110     5 × 22
     66
  -  66     3 × 22
```

4. $\boxed{30}$

```
        32
  27)864
  - 810    30 × 27
     54
  -  54     2 × 27
```

5. $\enclose{circle}{20}$
19
32)608
 − 320   10 × 32
   288
 − 288   9 × 32

6. $\enclose{circle}{15}$
17
44)748
 − 440   10 × 44
   308
 − 220   5 × 44
    88
 − 88   2 × 44

7. $\enclose{circle}{30}$
26
23)598
 − 460   20 × 23
   138
 − 138   6 × 23

8. $\enclose{circle}{32}$
34
19)646
 − 570   30 × 19
    76
 − 76   4 × 19

9. $\enclose{circle}{20}$
22
38)836
 − 760   20 × 38
    76
 − 76   2 × 38

10. $\enclose{circle}{20}$
21
18)378
 − 360   20 × 18
    18
 − 18   1 × 18

11. $\enclose{circle}{20}$
23
35)805
 − 700   20 × 35
   105
 − 105   3 × 35

12. $\enclose{circle}{20}$
16
24)384
 − 240   10 × 24
   144
 − 144   6 × 24

13. £24
14. £37
15. £26
16. £46
17. £39·5
18. £28
19. £53
20. £34
21. £46

Owl Answers may vary.

Page 6l

Dividing

1. $\enclose{circle}{£4}$
£4·23
30)126·90
 − 120   £4 × 30
   6·90
 − 6·00   20p × 30
   0·90
 − 0·90   3p × 30

2. $\enclose{circle}{£6}$
£6·46
20)129·20
 − 120   £6 × 20
   9·20
 − 8·00   40p × 20
   1·20
 − 1·20   6p × 20

3. $\enclose{circle}{£6}$
£5·78
40)231·20
 − 200   £5 × 40
   31·20
 − 30·00   75p × 40
   1·20
 −   1·20   3p × 40

4.

    (£8)

    £7·41

25)185·25

  − 175   £7 × 25

    10·25

  − 10·00   40p × 25

     0·25

 −   0·25   1p × 25

5.

    (£8)

    £8·26

31)256·06

  − 248   £8 × 31

    8·06

 − 6·20   20p × 31

    1·86

 − 1·86   6p × 31

6.

    (£8)

    £7·47

32)239·04

  − 224   £7 × 32

    15·04

 − 12·80   40p × 32

    2·24

 − 2·24   7p × 32

7.

    (£6)

    £5·79

21)121·59

  − 105   £5 × 21

    16·59

 − 14·70   70p × 21

    1·89

 − 1·89   9p × 21

8.

    (£8)

    £7·23

22)159·06

  − 154   £7 × 22

    5·06

 − 4·40   20p × 22

    0·66

 − 0·66   3p × 22

9.

    (£6)

    £6·84

28)191·52

  − 168   £6 × 28

    23·52

 − 22·40   80p × 28

    1·12

 − 1·12   4p × 28

Explore Answers may vary.

Page 62

Dividing decimals

Estimates may vary.

1.

    (10)

    13·3

4)53·2

  ⁻ 40   10 × 4

    13·2

 − 12   3 × 4

    1·2

 − 1·2   0·3 × 4

2.

    (20)

    18·4

3)55·2

  − 30   10 × 3

    25·2

 − 24   8 × 3

    1·2

 − 1·2   0·4 × 3

3.

    (15)

    14·7

6)88·2

  − 60   10 × 6

    28·2

 − 24   4 × 6

    4·2

 − 4·2   0·7 × 6

4. (13)

$$13{\cdot}2$$
$$4\overline{)52{\cdot}8}$$

$-\ 40$	10×4
$12{\cdot}8$	
$-\ 12$	3×4
$0{\cdot}8$	
$-\ 0{\cdot}8$	$0{\cdot}2 \times 4$

5. (12)

$$12{\cdot}3$$
$$3\overline{)36{\cdot}9}$$

$-\ 30$	10×3
$6{\cdot}9$	
$-\ 6$	2×3
$0{\cdot}9$	
$-\ 0{\cdot}9$	$0{\cdot}3 \times 3$

6. (15)

$$15{\cdot}1$$
$$5\overline{)75{\cdot}5}$$

$-\ 50$	10×5
$25{\cdot}5$	
$-\ 25$	5×5
$0{\cdot}5$	
$-\ 0{\cdot}5$	$0{\cdot}1 \times 5$

7. (15)

$$17{\cdot}2 \text{ km}$$
$$4\overline{)68{\cdot}8}$$

$-\ 40$	10×4
$28{\cdot}8$	
$-\ 28$	7×4
$0{\cdot}8$	
$-\ 0{\cdot}8$	$0{\cdot}2 \times 4$

8. (14)

$$14{\cdot}7 \text{ km}$$
$$3\overline{)44{\cdot}1}$$

$-\ 30$	10×3
$14{\cdot}1$	
$-\ 12$	4×3
$2{\cdot}1$	
$-\ 2{\cdot}1$	$0{\cdot}7 \times 3$

9. (10)

$$11{\cdot}3 \text{ km}$$
$$4\overline{)45{\cdot}2}$$

$-\ 40$	10×4
$5{\cdot}2$	
$-\ 4$	1×4
$1{\cdot}2$	
$-\ 1{\cdot}2$	$0{\cdot}3 \times 4$

10. (20)

$$23{\cdot}6 \text{ km}$$
$$3\overline{)70{\cdot}8}$$

$-\ 60$	20×3
$10{\cdot}8$	
$-\ 9$	3×3
$1{\cdot}8$	
$-\ 1{\cdot}8$	$0{\cdot}6 \times 3$

11. (25)

$$22{\cdot}7 \text{ km}$$
$$4\overline{)90{\cdot}8}$$

$-\ 80$	20×4
$10{\cdot}8$	
$-\ 8$	2×4
$2{\cdot}8$	
$-\ 2{\cdot}8$	$0{\cdot}7 \times 4$

12. (14)

$$13{\cdot}9 \text{ km}$$
$$3\overline{)41{\cdot}7}$$

$-\ 30$	10×3
$11{\cdot}7$	
$-\ 9$	3×3
$2{\cdot}7$	
$-\ 2{\cdot}7$	$0{\cdot}9 \times 3$

13. (12)

$$12{\cdot}7 \text{ km}$$
$$6\overline{)76{\cdot}2}$$

$-\ 60$	10×6
$16{\cdot}2$	
$-\ 12$	2×6
$4{\cdot}2$	
$-\ 4{\cdot}2$	$0{\cdot}7 \times 6$

14.

$$\textcircled{30}$$

$$\begin{array}{r} 26\cdot8\,\text{km} \\ 3\overline{)80\cdot4} \\ -\,60 \qquad 20\times3 \\ \hline 20\cdot4 \\ -\,18 \qquad 6\times3 \\ \hline 2\cdot4 \\ -\,2\cdot4 \qquad 0\cdot8\times3 \end{array}$$

15.

$$\textcircled{20}$$

$$\begin{array}{r} 18\cdot8\,\text{km} \\ 4\overline{)75\cdot2} \\ -\,40 \qquad 10\times4 \\ \hline 35\cdot2 \\ -\,32 \qquad 8\times4 \\ \hline 3\cdot2 \\ -\,3\cdot2 \qquad 0\cdot8\times4 \end{array}$$

Owl Answers may vary.

Page 63

Dividing decimals

1.

$$\textcircled{30}$$

$$\begin{array}{r} 28\cdot2\,\text{g} \\ 3\overline{)84\cdot6} \\ -\,60 \qquad 20\times3 \\ \hline 24\cdot6 \\ -\,24 \qquad 8\times3 \\ \hline 0\cdot6 \\ -\,0\cdot6 \qquad 0\cdot2\times3 \end{array}$$

2.

$$\textcircled{13}$$

$$\begin{array}{r} 13\cdot6\,\text{g} \\ 6\overline{)81\cdot6} \\ -\,60 \qquad 10\times6 \\ \hline 21\cdot6 \\ -\,18 \qquad 3\times6 \\ \hline 3\cdot6 \\ -\,3\cdot6 \qquad 0\cdot6\times6 \end{array}$$

3.

$$\textcircled{20}$$

$$\begin{array}{r} 19\cdot8\,\text{g} \\ 4\overline{)79\cdot2} \\ -\,40 \qquad 10\times4 \\ \hline 39\cdot2 \\ -\,36 \qquad 9\times4 \\ \hline 3\cdot2 \\ -\,3\cdot2 \qquad 0\cdot8\times4 \end{array}$$

4.

$$\textcircled{18}$$

$$\begin{array}{r} 17\cdot7\,\text{g} \\ 5\overline{)88\cdot5} \\ -\,50 \qquad 10\times5 \\ \hline 38\cdot5 \\ -\,35 \qquad 7\times5 \\ \hline 3\cdot5 \\ -\,3\cdot5 \qquad 0\cdot7\times5 \end{array}$$

5.

$$\textcircled{13}$$

$$\begin{array}{r} 12\cdot9\,\text{g} \\ 7\overline{)90\cdot3} \\ -\,70 \qquad 10\times7 \\ \hline 20\cdot3 \\ -\,14 \qquad 2\times7 \\ \hline 6\cdot3 \\ -\,6\cdot3 \qquad 0\cdot9\times7 \end{array}$$

6.

$$\textcircled{8}$$

$$\begin{array}{r} 8\cdot8\,\text{g} \\ 4\overline{)35\cdot2} \\ -\,32 \qquad 8\times4 \\ \hline 3\cdot2 \\ -\,3\cdot2 \qquad 0\cdot8\times4 \end{array}$$

7.

$$\textcircled{22}$$

$$\begin{array}{r} 22\cdot7\,\text{g} \\ 4\overline{)90\cdot8} \\ -\,80 \qquad 20\times4 \\ \hline 10\cdot8 \\ -\,8 \qquad 2\times4 \\ \hline 2\cdot8 \\ -\,2\cdot8 \qquad 0\cdot7\times4 \end{array}$$

8.

$$\textcircled{30}$$

$$\begin{array}{r} 29\cdot4\,\text{g} \\ 3\overline{)88\cdot2} \\ -\,60 \qquad 20\times3 \\ \hline 28\cdot2 \\ -\,27 \qquad 9\times3 \\ \hline 1\cdot2 \\ -\,1\cdot2 \qquad 0\cdot4\times3 \end{array}$$

9.

    (23)

    16·9 g

    4)67·6

    − 40   10 × 4

    27·6

    − 24   6 × 4

    3·6

    − 3·6   0·9 × 4

10. 14·7

11. 23·6

12. 12·2

13. 11·8

14. 16·4

15. 32·3

16. 21·6

17. 13·7

18. 23·9

Owl

  1. approximately 36

  2. approximately 74

  3. approximately 51

  4. approximately 57

  5. approximately 78

  6. approximately 114

  7. approximately 44

  8. approximately 34

  9. approximately 59

Page 64

Dividing decimals

1.

    (2)

    1·82 m

    4)7·28

    − 4   1   × 4

    3·28

    − 3·20   0·8 × 4

    0·08

    − 0·08   0·02 × 4

2.

    (1)

    1·46 m

    6)8·76

    − 6   1   × 6

    2·76

    − 2·40   0·4 × 6

    0·36

    − 0·36   0·06 × 6

3.

    (1)

    1·13 m

    8)9·04

    − 8   1   × 8

    1·04

    − 0·8   0·1 × 8

    0·24

    − 0·24   0·03 × 8

4.

    (3)

    2·74 m

    3)8·22

    − 6   2   × 3

    2·22

    − 2·10   0·7 × 3

    0·12

    − 0·12   0·04 × 3

5.

    (1)

    1·08 m

    9)9·72

    − 9   1   × 9

    0·72

    − 0·72   0·08 × 9

6.

    (1)

    1·39 m

    5)6·95

    − 5   1   × 5

    1·95

    − 1·5   0·3 × 5

    0·45

    − 0·45   0·09 × 5

  7. 27·34 m

  8. 18·46 m

  9. 13·64 m

10. 12·82 m

11. 32·14 m
12. 11·78 m
13. 21·23 m
14. 12·44 m
15. 26·46 m

Owl Answers may vary. One possible
answer is that the three equal sides
are 2·14 m each, and the shorter side
is 2 m. As long as the children subtract
a length for the shorter side so that
an amount exactly divisible by 3 is left
for the three longer sides, the answer
should be correct, e.g the shorter side
could = 0·32 m, leaving 8·1 m, so the
three equal sides are 2·7 m each.

Page 65
Dividing decimals

1.
```
      (8)
    8·34
  4)33·36
  − 32        8    × 4
   1·36
  − 1·20      0·3  × 4
   0·16
  − 0·16      0·04 × 4
```

2.
```
      (6)
    6·28
  3)18·84
  − 18        6    × 3
   0·84
  − 0·60      0·2  × 3
   0·24
  − 0·24      0·08 × 3
```

3.
```
      (7)
    7·46
  6)44·76
  − 42        7    × 6
   2·76
  − 2·40      0·4  × 6
   0·36
  − 0·36      0·06 × 6
```

4.
```
      (9)
    9·53
  8)76·24
  − 72        9    × 8
   4·24
  − 4·00      0·5  × 8
   0·24
  − 0·24      0·03 × 8
```

5.
```
      (7)
    6·72
  7)47·04
  − 42        6    × 7
   5·04
  − 4·90      0·7  × 7
   0·14
  − 0·14      0·02 × 7
```

6.
```
      (8)
    8·47
  3)25·41
  − 24        8    × 3
   1·41
  − 1·20      0·4  × 3
   0·21
  − 0·21      0·07 × 3
```

7.
```
      (13)
    12·84
  4)51·36
  − 48        12   × 4
   3·36
  − 3·20      0·8  × 4
   0·16
  − 0·16      0·04 × 4
```

8.
```
      (26)
    26·32
  5)131·60
  − 130       26   × 5
   1·60
  − 1·50      0·3  × 5
   0·10
  − 0·10      0·02 × 5
```

Textbook

9. $\boxed{20}$

$$18\cdot46$$
$$9\overline{)166\cdot14}$$
$$-\ 162 \qquad 18 \quad \times\,9$$
$$\overline{4\cdot14}$$
$$-\ \underline{3\cdot60} \qquad 0\cdot4 \ \times\,9$$
$$\overline{0\cdot54}$$
$$-\ \underline{0\cdot54} \qquad 0\cdot06\times 9$$

10. $856\cdot8 \div 40 = 85\cdot68 \div 4 = 21\cdot42$
11. $883\cdot8 \div 60 = 88\cdot38 \div 6 = 14\cdot73$
12. $97\cdot53 \div 30 = 9\cdot753 \div 3 = 3\cdot251$
13. $886\cdot9 \div 70 = 88\cdot69 \div 7 = 12\cdot67$
14. $942\cdot4 \div 80 = 94\cdot24 \div 8 = 11\cdot78$
15. $975\cdot6 \div 90 = 97\cdot56 \div 9 = 10\cdot84$
Owl The trick is to times both parts by
10, e.g. $18\cdot36 \div 0\cdot3 = 183\cdot6 \div 3$
$= 61\cdot2$.

Block E3

Page 66
Proportion

1. 4 out of 12
$\frac{4}{12} = \frac{1}{3}$
2. 5 out of 15
$\frac{5}{15} = \frac{1}{3}$
3. 14 out of 21
$\frac{14}{21} = \frac{2}{3}$
4. 12 out of 16
$\frac{12}{16} = \frac{3}{4}$
5. 10 out of 15
$\frac{10}{15} = \frac{2}{3}$
6. 1 out of 8
$= \frac{1}{8}$
7. 21 out of 24
$\frac{21}{24} = \frac{7}{8}$
8. 2 out of 8
$\frac{2}{8} = \frac{1}{4}$
9. 9 out of 12
$\frac{9}{12} = \frac{3}{4}$

Proportion of non-red marbles:
1. $\frac{2}{3}$
2. $\frac{2}{3}$
3. $\frac{1}{3}$
4. $\frac{1}{4}$
5. $\frac{1}{3}$
6. $\frac{7}{8}$
7. $\frac{1}{8}$
8. $\frac{3}{4}$
9. $\frac{1}{4}$
10. 2 out of 12
$\frac{2}{12} = \frac{1}{6}$
11. 1 out of 12
$= \frac{1}{12}$
12. 2 out of 12
$\frac{2}{12} = \frac{1}{6}$
13. 2 out of 12
$\frac{2}{12} = \frac{1}{6}$
14. 9 out of 12
$\frac{9}{12} = \frac{3}{4}$
15. 5 out of 12
$= \frac{5}{12}$
16. 5 out of 12
$= \frac{5}{12}$
17. 3 out of 12
$\frac{3}{12} = \frac{1}{4}$
18. 6 out of 12
$\frac{6}{12} = \frac{1}{2}$
Owl Answers may vary. Possible
answers include: $\frac{2}{5}, \frac{4}{10}, \frac{6}{15}, \frac{8}{20}, \frac{10}{25}$, etc.

Page 67
Proportion

1. 5 out of 15
$\frac{5}{15} = \frac{1}{3}$
2. 6 out of 15
$\frac{6}{15} = \frac{2}{5}$
3. 6 out of 15
$\frac{6}{15} = \frac{2}{5}$

4. 3 out of 15
$\frac{3}{15} = \frac{1}{5}$
5. 10 out of 15
$\frac{10}{15} = \frac{2}{3}$
6. 1 out of 15
$= \frac{1}{15}$
7. 0 out of 15
$= 0$
8. 8 out of 15
$= \frac{8}{15}$
9. 2 out of 15
$= \frac{2}{15}$
10. 4 out of 15
$= \frac{4}{15}$
11. 9 out of 15
$\frac{9}{15} = \frac{3}{5}$
12. 3 out of 15
$\frac{3}{15} = \frac{1}{5}$

Owl Questions giving proportions greater than 50%: 5, 8 and 11.

Page 68
Proportion

1. $\frac{1}{4}$ of 24 = 6 finches
2. $\frac{1}{4}$ of 32 = 8 finches
3. $\frac{1}{4}$ of 16 = 4 finches
4. $\frac{1}{4}$ of 48 = 12 finches
5. $\frac{1}{4}$ of 120 = 30 finches

If the proportion is 1 out of 8:

1. $\frac{1}{8}$ of 24 = 3 robins
2. $\frac{1}{8}$ of 32 = 4 robins
3. $\frac{1}{8}$ of 16 = 2 robins
4. $\frac{1}{8}$ of 48 = 6 robins
5. $\frac{1}{8}$ of 120 = 15 robins
6. 3 out of 8
6 out of 16
16 cars go past
7. 3 out of 8
9 out of 24
24 cars go past
8. 3 out of 8
30 out of 80
80 cars go past

9. 3 out of 8
15 out of 40
40 cars go past
10. 3 out of 8
12 out of 32
32 cars go past
11. 3 out of 8
24 out of 64
64 cars go past
12. 3 out of 8
66 out of 176
176 cars go past
13. 3 out of 8 cars speed
5 out of 8 cars don't speed
5 out of 8 cars = 25
3 out of 8 cars must = 15
40 cars go past altogether
14. 3 out of 8 cars speed
5 out of 8 cars don't speed
5 out of 8 cars = 55
3 out of 8 cars must = 33
88 cars go past altogether
Proportion of speeding cars = 1 out of 4:
100 cars must pass for the number of speeding cars to = 25.
Owl Answers may vary.

Page 69
Proportion

1. 12 cats
2. 10 cats
3. 6 cats
4. 1 cat
5. 18 cats
6. 800 cats
7. 11 cats
8. 72 cats
9. 606 cats
10. 60 cats
11. 28
12. 160
13. 15
Owl Answers may vary.

Page 70

Ratio

1. $\frac{5}{8}$, 5:3
2. $\frac{2}{9}$, 2:7
3. $\frac{5}{12}$, 5:7
4. $\frac{1}{6}$, 1:5
5. $\frac{1}{10}$, 1:9
6. $\frac{5}{8}$, 5:3
7. 4 red
8. 8 red
9. 40 red
10. 20 red
11. 28 red
12. 16 red
13. 120 red
14. 4000 red
15. 360 red

Owl 4, 8, 12, 16, etc.

Page 71

Ratio

1. $\frac{5}{10} = \frac{1}{2}$
   5:5 = 1:1
2. $\frac{3}{9} = \frac{1}{3}$
   3:6 = 1:2
3. $\frac{3}{8}$
   3:5
4. $\frac{6}{9} = \frac{2}{3}$
   6:3 = 2:1
5. $\frac{4}{8} = \frac{1}{2}$
   4:4 = 1:1
6. 3 + 5 = 8
   10 tiles
7. 3 + 5 = 8
   25 tiles
8. 3 + 5 = 8
   500 tiles
9. 3 + 5 = 8
   15 tiles
10. 3 + 5 = 8
    35 tiles
11. 3 + 5 = 8
    200 tiles

Owl Answers may vary.

Page 72

Ratio

1. 6 red
   9 blue
2. 12 red
   18 blue
3. 20 red
   30 blue
4. 2 red
   3 blue
5. 40 red
   60 blue
6. 24 red
   36 blue
7. true
8. false
9. false
10. true
11. true
12. true

Owl Answers may vary.

Page 73

Ratio

1. 4 eggs
   200 g fat
   600 g sugar
   800 g flour
2. 2 eggs
   100 g fat
   300 g sugar
   400 g flour
3. 1 egg
   50 g fat
   150 g sugar
   200 g flour
4. 8 eggs
   400 g fat
   1200 g sugar
   1600 g flour

5. 5 eggs
   250 g fat
   750 g sugar
   1000 g flour
6. 6
7. 60 ml of milk; 210 ml of tea
8. 0·75 kg

Owl There could be any number of children in the class, as long as it is exactly divisible by 5. Answers may vary.

Page 74
Prime numbers

1.–6. 10 prime numbers between 1 and 30

~~1~~	2	3	~~4~~	5	~~6~~	7	~~8~~	~~9~~	~~10~~
11	~~12~~	13	~~14~~	~~15~~	~~16~~	17	~~18~~	19	~~20~~
~~21~~	~~22~~	23	~~24~~	~~25~~	~~26~~	~~27~~	~~28~~	29	~~30~~
31	~~32~~	~~33~~	~~34~~	~~35~~	~~36~~	37	~~38~~	~~39~~	~~40~~
41	~~42~~	43	~~44~~	~~45~~	~~46~~	47	~~48~~	~~49~~	~~50~~
~~51~~	~~52~~	53	~~54~~	~~55~~	~~56~~	~~57~~	~~58~~	59	~~60~~
61	~~62~~	~~63~~	~~64~~	~~65~~	~~66~~	67	~~68~~	~~69~~	~~70~~
71	~~72~~	73	~~74~~	~~75~~	~~76~~	~~77~~	~~78~~	79	~~80~~
~~81~~	~~82~~	83	~~84~~	~~85~~	~~86~~	~~87~~	~~88~~	89	~~90~~
~~91~~	~~92~~	~~93~~	~~94~~	~~95~~	~~96~~	97	~~98~~	~~99~~	~~100~~

7. No. There are 15 prime numbers between 1–50 and 10 between 50–100.
8. a) 8
   b) 4
   c) 5
   d) 5

Explore Five have a last digit of 1; one has a last digit of 2; seven have a last digit of 3; none have a last digit of 4; one has a last digit of 5; none have a last digit of 6; six have a last digit of 7; none have a last digit of 8; 5 have a last digit of 9. The most common last digit of prime numbers below 100 is 3.

Page 75
Prime numbers

1. yes
2. yes
3. yes
4. no
5. no
6. yes
7. yes
8. no
9. no
10. no
11. no
12. no
13. 7, 3, 5, 11
14. 13, 17, 19
15. 29, 31, 41
16. 43, 47
17. 13
18. 11
19. 5
20. 17
21. 23
22. 29
23. 31
24. 37
25. 43
26. 53
27. 61
28. 29
29. 37
30. 71
31. 83
32. 47

Owl
4. 29
5. 13 or 17
8. 19 or 23
9. 37 or 41
10. 97
11. 31
12. 73

Explore 13 and 31; 37 and 73; 79 and 97

Page 76

Prime numbers

1. false
2. true
3. true
4. false
5. false
6. true
7. true
8. false
9. true
10. true
11. true
12. true

First Explore Answers may vary.
Second Explore 17 and 73; 19 and 71; 23 and 67; 29 and 61; 31 and 59; 37 and 53; 43 and 47

Page 77

Prime numbers

1. 37
2. 53
3. 29
4. 37
5. 31
6. 71 or 73 or 79

First Explore Answers may vary.
Second Explore

57	58	59	60	61	62	63	64	65
56	31	32	33	34	35	36	37	66
55	30	13	14	15	16	17	38	67
54	29	12	3	4	5	18	39	68
53	28	11	2	1	6	19	40	69
52	27	10	9	8	7	20	41	70
51	26	25	24	23	22	21	42	71
50	49	48	47	46	45	44	43	72
	80	79	78	77	76	75	74	73

Page 78

Prime factors

1.

2	40
2	20
2	10
5	5
	1

2.

2	12
2	6
3	3
	1

3.

2	16
2	8
2	4
2	2
	1

4.

2	30
3	15
5	5
	1

5.

2	24
2	12
2	6
3	3
	1

6.

2	20
2	10
5	5
	1

7.

2	52
2	26
13	13
	1

8.

5	35
7	7
	1

Prime factors of each number:
1. prime factors of 40: 2 × 2 × 2 × 5
2. prime factors of 12: 2 × 2 × 3

3. prime factors of 16: 2 × 2 × 2 × 2
4. prime factors of 30: 2 × 3 × 5
5. prime factors of 24: 2 × 2 × 2 × 3
6. prime factors of 20: 2 × 2 × 5
7. prime factors of 52: 2 × 2 × 13
8. prime factors of 35: 5 × 7
9. 2 × 2 × 2
10. 2 × 7
11. 2 × 3 × 3
12. 3 × 3 × 3
13. 2 × 2 × 7
14. 2 × 13
15. 2 × 2 × 2 × 2 × 2
16. 3 × 3 × 5
17.

Number	Prime factors
20	2 × 2 × 5
21	3 × 7
22	2 × 11
23	23
24	2 × 2 × 2 × 3
25	5 × 5
26	2 × 13
27	3 × 3 × 3
28	2 × 2 × 7
29	29
30	2 × 3 × 5
31	31
32	2 × 2 × 2 × 2 × 2
33	3 × 11
34	2 × 17
35	5 × 7
36	2 × 2 × 3 × 3
37	37
38	2 × 19
39	3 × 13
40	2 × 2 × 2 × 5

Owl Answers may vary.

Page 79

Prime factors

1.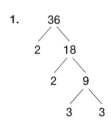

2.

3.

4.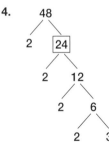

5.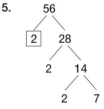

6.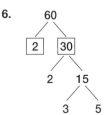

Prime factors:
1. $2 \times 2 \times 3 \times 3$
2. $2 \times 5 \times 5$
3. $2 \times 2 \times 7$
4. $2 \times 2 \times 2 \times 2 \times 3$
5. $2 \times 2 \times 2 \times 7$
6. $2 \times 2 \times 3 \times 5$
7. 2×19
8. $2 \times 3 \times 3$
9. 3×17
10. $2 \times 3 \times 3 \times 3$
11. 3×19
12. $2 \times 3 \times 7$
13. $2 \times 2 \times 2 \times 13$
14. $2 \times 5 \times 7$
15. $2 \times 2 \times 2 \times 2 \times 3 \times 3$
16. $2 \times 2 \times 2 \times 3 \times 5$
17. $2 \times 2 \times 3 \times 3 \times 3$
18. $2 \times 5 \times 5 \times 5$

Explore Answers may vary.

Page 80

Prime factors

1. $2 \times 2 \times 3 = 12$
2. $2 \times 3 \times 5 = 30$
3. $2 \times 3 \times 3 \times 3 = 54$
4. $3 \times 5 \times 7 = 105$
5. $2 \times 3 \times 11 = 66$
6. $3 \times 3 \times 7 = 63$
7. $2 \times 3 \times 5 \times 7 = 210$
8. $2 \times 2 \times 2 \times 2 \times 2 = 32$
9. $3 \times 3 \times 3 = 27$
10. $5 \times 5 \times 5 = 125$
11. $3 \times 7 \times 11 = 231$
12. $2 \times 5 \times 17 = 170$

First Explore Answers may vary.
Second Explore Answers may vary.

Block AI

PCM I

Multiplying by 10, 100 and 1000

1. 4·3
2. 5·6
3. 7·2
4. 8·4
5. 10
6. 100
7. 5·23
8. 10
9. 0·85
10. 4·06
11. 10
12. 100
13. 12·7
14. 6·85
15. 11·27
16. 1000
17. 100
18. 12·75

PCM 2

Multiplying using doubling

1. 6·8
2. 552
3. 45·2
4. 680
5. 312
6. 2880
7. 10 420
8. 8·74
9. 8320
10. 505·6
11. 31 200
12. 1684

PCM 3

Dividing by 10, 100 and 1000

Th	H	T	U	·	t	h
		4	3	·	2	
		1	5	·	6	
			3	·	8	5
			0	·	7	2
			0	·	1	6
			0	·	4	7
			1	·	6	
			0	·	0	8
			0	·	0	9
			1	·	7	6

PCM 4

Dividing using halving

1. 3·07
2. 1·18
3. 1·155
4. 0·368
5. 1·81
6. 1·185
7. 1·921
8. 1·622
9. 0·951
10. 6·7
11. 23·9
12. 10·525

PCM 5

Table facts

1. 48
2. 7
3. 28
4. 7

5. 8
6. 24
7. 8
8. 49
9. 81
10. 9
11. 9
12. 20
13. 40
14. 7
15. 6
16. 36
17. 54
18. 3
19. 5
20. 64
21. 18
22. 5
23. 5
24. 36

PCM 6
Multiplying using table facts

1. 210
2. 360
3. 240
4. 350
5. 490
6. 240
7. 630
8. 540
9. 2800
10. 2000
11. 6400
12. 4800
13. 27 000
14. 720
15. 4200
16. 450
17. 1800
18. 3600
19. 560
20. 320

PCM 7
Remainders as fractions

1. $9\frac{1}{3}$
2. $23\frac{1}{2}$
3. $6\frac{3}{4}$
4. $7\frac{3}{7}$
5. $4\frac{5}{6}$
6. $7\frac{1}{3}$
7. $8\frac{3}{5}$
8. $4\frac{3}{4}$
9. $16\frac{1}{2}$
10. $5\frac{1}{3}$
11. $7\frac{1}{8}$
12. $6\frac{1}{3}$
13. $9\frac{3}{4}$
14. $5\frac{1}{7}$
15. $5\frac{2}{3}$
16. $5\frac{3}{5}$
17. $9\frac{1}{6}$
18. $6\frac{3}{7}$

PCM 8
Remainders as decimals

1. Answer provided
2. C
3. D
4. B
5. H
6. F
7. J
8. O
9. A
10. E
11. I
12. L
13. P
14. K
15. R
16. Q
17. M
18. G

Block BI

PCM 9

Multiplying odds and evens

even × even

×	1	2	3	4	5	6
1	1	2	3	4	5	6
2	2	4	6	8	10	12
3	3	6	9	12	15	18
4	4	8	12	16	20	24
5	5	10	15	20	25	30
6	6	12	18	24	30	36

odd × odd

×	1	2	3	4	5	6
1	1	2	3	4	5	6
2	2	4	6	8	10	12
3	3	6	9	12	15	18
4	4	8	12	16	20	24
5	5	10	15	20	25	30
6	6	12	18	24	30	36

even × odd

×	1	2	3	4	5	6
1	1	2	3	4	5	6
2	2	4	6	8	10	12
3	3	6	9	12	15	18
4	4	8	12	16	20	24
5	5	10	15	20	25	30
6	6	1 2	18	24	30	36

odd × even

×	1	2	3	4	5	6
1	1	2	3	4	5	6
2	2	4	6	8	10	12
3	3	6	9	12	15	18
4	4	8	12	16	20	24
5	5	10	15	20	25	30
6	6	12	18	24	30	36

Answers for the rules may vary. A possible answer is:

even × even = even
odd × odd = odd
even × odd = even
odd × even = even

PCM 10

Odds and evens

1. O
2. E
3. O
4. E
5. E
6. O
7. E
8. O
9. E
10. E
11. O
12. E
13. E
14. E
15. E
16. E

PCM 11

Multiples

1. 45, 50, 55, 65, 70
2. 27, 30, 33, 36, 42
3. 18, 27, 45, 54, 72, 81
4. 20, 24, 28, 32, 36, 40
5. 24, 30, 36, 48, 54, 60
6. 44, 55, 66, 77, 88, 110
7. 30, 45, 60, 75, 105, 120
8. 25, 50, 100, 125, 175, 200
9. 40, 120, 200, 240, 280, 320

PCM 12

Smallest common multiples

	2	3	4	5	6	7	8	9	10	11
2										
3	6									
4	4	12								
5	10	15	20							
6	6	6	12	30						
7	14	21	28	35	42					
8	8	24	8	40	24	56				
9	18	9	36	45	18	63	72			
10	10	30	20	10	30	70	40	90		
11	22	33	44	55	66	77	88	99	110	

PCM 13

Quadrilaterals

1. rectangle
2. trapezium
3. parallelogram
4. parallelogram
5. square
6. trapezium
7. trapezium
8. parallelogram
9. trapezium
10. parallelogram
11. square
12. parallelogram
13. trapezium
14. rectangle
15. trapezium
16. parallelogram

PCM 14

Polygons

1.

2.

3.

4.

5.

6.

7.

8.

9.

10.

11.

12. or

13.

14. or

15.

16.

Block CI

PCM I5
Pictograms

Answers will vary.

PCM I6
Grouped data

1. 6–10
2. 21–25
3. 16–20
4. 11–15
5. 3

6. 9
7. 19
8. 14
9. 25
10. 28
11. 32
12. 14
13. 46
14. 47
15. 60

PCM I7
Grouped data

Minutes	Tally	Frequency
0–15	|||	3
16–30	ЖЖ ЖЖ |||	13
31–45	ЖЖ ЖЖ		11
46–60	ЖЖ ||	7
61–75	ЖЖ |||	8
76–90	ЖЖ ЖЖ ||||	14

PCM I8
Centimetres and inches

Answers will vary.

PCM I9
Kilometres and miles

1. 64
2. 123
3. 74
4. 82
5. 490
6. 131
7. 379
8. 1062
9. 264
10. 342

PCM 20
Parcel weights

1. 2500
2. 1700
3. 1250
4. 7300
5. 2450
6. 750
7. 1·5 or $1\frac{1}{2}$
8. 0·75 or $\frac{3}{4}$
9. 4·7
10. 3·6
11. 5·25 or $5\frac{1}{4}$
12. 0·32

PCM 2I
Kilograms, grams, pounds, ounces

1. =
2. >
3. <
4. =
5. >
6. >
7. <
8. <
9. >
10. <
11. >
12. >
13. =
14. <
15. <
16. >
17. =
18. >

Block DI

PCM 22
Angles at a point

1. 38°, 142°, 142°
2. 122°, 58°, 58°
3. 79°, 101°, 101°
4. 154°, 26°, 26°
5. 29°, 151°, 151°

PCM 23
Estimating angles

	a	b	c	d	e	f
Estimated						
Measured	30°	110°	55°	90°	25°	130°
Difference						

Answers for estimates and differences will vary.

PCM 24
Angles in a triangle

1. 52°
2. 19°
3. 68°
4. 25°
5. 66°
6. 44°
7. 62°
8. 105°
9. 127°
10. 136°
11. 14°

PCM 25
Row and column totals

4	6	7	8	25
7	6	5	9	27
8	4	9	9	30
9	5	4	6	24
28	21	25	32	

21	32	52	43	148
36	51	24	45	156
28	47	31	56	162
44	25	54	37	160
129	155	161	181	

300	400	100	600	1400
700	500	300	700	2200
600	100	200	400	1300
300	700	500	600	2100
1900	1700	1100	2300	

d	169	527	238	376
93	76	434	145	283
471	302	56	233	95
184	15	343	54	192
532	363	5	294	156
615	446	88	377	239

PCM 26
Adding and subtracting

1. 9·3
2. 6·8
3. 2·5
4. 6·8
5. 6·1
6. 9·2
7. 9·7
8. 1·8
9. 3·9
10. 2·2
11. 2·1
12. 6·9
13. 8·9
14. 4·1
15. 2·25
16. 3·17
17. 6·75
18. 5·82
19. 1·95
20. 1·16

PCM 27
Differences

d	18	38	83	74
29	11	9	54	45
41	23	3	42	33
56	38	18	27	18
62	44	24	21	12
97	79	59	14	23

PCM 28
Subtracting

Answers will vary.

Block EI
PCM 29
Doubling and halving

94	166	56
134	148	68
182	112	106

43	69	33
57	49	76
23	88	39

14·8	5·2	17·8
23·8	13·4	27·6
11·6	31·4	8·6

PCM 30
Half-price sale

1. £430
2. £205
3. £165
4. £475
5. £370
6. £145
7. £615

8. £540
9. £785
10. £915
11. £585
12. £730

PCM 3I
Multiplying by doubling

1. 21, 42, 84
2. 30, 60, 120
3. 56, 112, 224
4. 36, 72, 144
5. 32, 64, 128
6. 42, 6 × 14 = 84, 6 × 28 = 168
7. 27, 3 × 18 = 54, 3 × 36 = 108
8. 48, 6 × 16 = 96, 6 × 32 = 192
9. 72, 8 × 18 = 144, 8 × 36 = 288
10. 63, 9 × 14 = 126, 9 × 28 = 252

PCM 32
Multiplying by 23

1. 23
2. 46
3. 92
4. 184
5. 368
6. 736
7. 414
8. 207
9. 253
10. 391
11. 805
12. 1104
13. 483
14. 161
15. 943
16. 1288

PCM 33
Mixed numbers and improper fractions

1. Answer provided
2. $\frac{10}{3}$

3. $\frac{22}{5}$
4. $\frac{29}{4}$
5. $\frac{11}{6}$
6. $\frac{31}{7}$
7. $\frac{17}{3}$
8. $\frac{29}{8}$
9. $\frac{14}{5}$
10. $\frac{107}{10}$
11. $\frac{51}{7}$
12. $\frac{27}{4}$
13. $\frac{29}{3}$
14. $\frac{26}{5}$
15. $\frac{35}{4}$
16. $\frac{29}{9}$
17. $\frac{18}{7}$
18. $\frac{59}{8}$
19. $\frac{41}{6}$
20. $\frac{41}{7}$

PCM 34
Mixed numbers and improper fractions

1. <
2. <
3. <
4. =
5. >
6. <
7. =
8. >
9. >
10. <
11. <
12. >
13. <
14. =
15. >
16. >

PCM 35
Equivalent fractions game

No answers required.

PCM 36
Fractions in simplest form

1. $\frac{3}{5}$
2. $\frac{2}{3}$
3. $\frac{3}{4}$
4. $\frac{7}{10}$
5. $\frac{2}{5}$
6. $\frac{3}{8}$
7. $\frac{5}{6}$
8. $\frac{2}{7}$
9. $\frac{4}{5}$
10. $\frac{1}{4}$
11. $\frac{4}{9}$
12. $\frac{7}{8}$
13. $\frac{2}{3}$
14. $\frac{1}{4}$
15. $\frac{3}{7}$
16. $\frac{1}{6}$
17. $\frac{3}{8}$
18. $\frac{3}{5}$
19. $\frac{1}{4}$
20. $\frac{4}{9}$
21. $\frac{9}{10}$
22. $\frac{5}{8}$
23. $\frac{4}{7}$
24. $\frac{5}{6}$

PCM 37
Ordering fractions

1. $\frac{1}{2} = \frac{18}{36}, \frac{4}{9} = \frac{16}{36}, \frac{17}{36} = \frac{17}{36}$
   $\frac{3}{4} = \frac{27}{36}, \frac{5}{6} = \frac{30}{36}, \frac{2}{3} = \frac{24}{30}$
   $\frac{4}{9}, \frac{17}{36}, \frac{1}{2}, \frac{2}{3}, \frac{3}{4}, \frac{5}{6}$
2. $\frac{7}{16} = \frac{14}{32}, \frac{3}{4} = \frac{24}{32}, \frac{5}{8} = \frac{20}{32},$
   $\frac{17}{32} = \frac{17}{32}, \frac{1}{2} = \frac{16}{32}, \frac{3}{8} = \frac{12}{32}$
   $\frac{3}{8}, \frac{7}{16}, \frac{1}{2}, \frac{17}{32}, \frac{5}{8}, \frac{3}{4}$
3. $\frac{3}{10} = \frac{6}{20}, \frac{1}{2} = \frac{10}{20}, \frac{3}{4} = \frac{15}{20},$
   $\frac{7}{10} = \frac{14}{20}, \frac{3}{5} = \frac{12}{20}, \frac{13}{20} = \frac{13}{20}$
   $\frac{3}{10}, \frac{1}{2}, \frac{3}{5}, \frac{13}{20}, \frac{7}{10}, \frac{3}{4}$
4. $\frac{3}{5}$ (£18)
5. Dinesh scored 4
6. $\frac{1}{6}$

PCM 38
Ordering fractions

1. $\frac{9}{12} > \frac{8}{12}$
2. $\frac{4}{10} < \frac{5}{10}$
3. $\frac{16}{20} > \frac{15}{20}$
4. $\frac{7}{10} > \frac{6}{10}$
5. $\frac{10}{15} < \frac{12}{15}$
6. $\frac{9}{12} < \frac{10}{12}$
7. $\frac{20}{24} < \frac{21}{24}$
8. $\frac{16}{18} > \frac{15}{18}$

PCM 39
Ordering and converting fractions

Answers will vary.

PCM 40
Converting fractions

1. $\frac{2}{3} = \frac{8}{12}, \frac{3}{4} = \frac{9}{12}$
   $\frac{8}{12} + \frac{9}{12} = \frac{17}{12}$
   $\frac{17}{12} = 1\frac{5}{12}$
2. $\frac{4}{8} = \frac{12}{24}, \frac{5}{6} = \frac{20}{24}$
   $\frac{12}{24} + \frac{20}{24} = \frac{32}{24}$
   $\frac{32}{24} = 1\frac{8}{24}$ or $1\frac{1}{3}$
3. $\frac{1}{2} = \frac{9}{18}, \frac{2}{9} = \frac{4}{18}$
   $\frac{9}{18} + \frac{4}{18} = \frac{13}{18}$
4. $\frac{3}{5} = \frac{21}{35}, \frac{5}{7} = \frac{25}{35}$
   $\frac{21}{35} + \frac{25}{35} = \frac{46}{35}$
   $\frac{46}{35} = 1\frac{11}{35}$
5. $\frac{2}{4} = \frac{4}{8}, \frac{3}{8} = \frac{3}{8}$
   $\frac{4}{8} + \frac{3}{8} = \frac{7}{8}$
6. $\frac{1}{3} = \frac{2}{6}, \frac{7}{6} = \frac{7}{6}$
   $\frac{2}{6} + \frac{7}{6} = \frac{9}{6}$
   $\frac{9}{6} = 1\frac{3}{6}$ or $1\frac{1}{2}$
7. $\frac{7}{10} = \frac{7}{10}, \frac{4}{5} = \frac{8}{10}$
   $\frac{7}{10} + \frac{8}{10} = \frac{15}{10}$
   $\frac{15}{10} = 1\frac{5}{10}$ or $1\frac{1}{2}$

8. $\frac{5}{6} = \frac{10}{12}, \frac{1}{4} = \frac{3}{12}$

$\frac{10}{12} + \frac{3}{12} = \frac{13}{12}$

$\frac{13}{12} = 1\frac{1}{12}$

9. $\frac{8}{9} = \frac{56}{63}, \frac{1}{7} = \frac{9}{63}$

$\frac{56}{63} + \frac{9}{63} = \frac{65}{63}$

$\frac{65}{63} = 1\frac{2}{63}$

10. $\frac{1}{4} = \frac{5}{20}, \frac{3}{5} = \frac{12}{20}$

$\frac{5}{20} + \frac{12}{20} = \frac{17}{20}$

11. $\frac{3}{7} = \frac{24}{56}, \frac{2}{8} = \frac{14}{56}$

$\frac{24}{56} + \frac{14}{56} = \frac{38}{56}$

$\frac{38}{56} = \frac{19}{28}$

12. $\frac{2}{5} = \frac{12}{30}, \frac{5}{6} = \frac{25}{30}$

$\frac{12}{30} + \frac{25}{30} = \frac{37}{30}$

$\frac{37}{30} = 1\frac{7}{30}$

Block A2

PCM 41
Rounding game

Answers will vary.

PCM 42
Rounding table

1. 5000, 4700, 4730
2. 6000, 5700, 5680
3. 3000, 2900, 2940
4. 6000, 6000, 6050
5. 5000, 5300, 5310
6. 10 000, 9700, 9730
7. 11 000, 11 300, 11 260
8. 13 000, 13 500, 13 470
9. 30 000, 29 500, 29 530
10. 186 000, 186 100, 186 080
11. 297 000, 297 500, 297 480
12. 1 587 000, 1 586 700, 1 586 720

PCM 43
Rounding decimals game

Answers will vary.

PCM 44
Rounding decimals

1. 7·24
2. 4·87
3. 2·47 or 2·48
4. 8·72 or 8·74
5. 4·72
6. 7·48
7. 8·27
8. 2·87
9. 7·82 or 7·84
10. 8·24
11. 4·82
12. 2·78 or 2·84
13. 8·47
14. 7·42
15. 2·74
16. 4·27 or 4·28
17. 7·28
18. 8·42

PCM 45
Ordering

1. <
2. >
3. >
4. =
5. >
6. <
7. >
8. <
9. <
10. >
11. <
12. >
13. >
14. >
15. <
16. <

PCM 46
Half-way numbers

1. 4·35
2. 1·8

3.	6·1
4.	7·15
5.	8·15
6.	0·55
7.	3·14
8.	5·22
9.	0·98
10.	1·31
11.	3·24
12.	4·75
13.	5·25
14.	6·145
15.	8·635
16.	7·129
17.	0·342
18.	5·289

PCM 47

Factor challenge

Answers may vary. Possible answers include:
12, 15, 12, 55, 42, 14, 24, 45
14, 51, 24, 55, 12, 21, 24, 54

PCM 48

Numbers of factors

Answers will vary. Possible answers include:

two factors	three factors	four factors	five factors	six factors	seven factors	eight factors
11	4	10	16	12	64	24
17	9	21	81	20		30
23	25	27		28		40
31	49	33		32		42
47		58		44		
53		46		52		
		51				

Answers about the patterns may vary.

Possible answers include:
prime numbers have two factors;
square numbers have an odd number of factors.

Block B2

PCM 49

Multiplying

Answers will vary.

PCM 50

Multiplication challenge

Answers will vary.

PCM 51

Multiplying by nearly 50, 100…

1.	1862
2.	1326
3.	988
4.	2016
5.	3838
6.	7722
7.	2646
8.	3162
9.	1794
10.	684
11.	608
12.	1562

PCM 52

Closest to 4000

1. Answer provided
2. $50 \times 83 = 4150$, $51 \times 83 = 4233$
3. $100 \times 42 = 4200$, $98 \times 42 = 4116$
4. $50 \times 78 = 3900$, $52 \times 78 = 4056$
5. $50 \times 82 = 4100$, $48 \times 82 = 3936$
6. $44 \times 100 = 4400$, $44 \times 97 = 4268$
7. $100 \times 39 = 3900$, $102 \times 39 = 3978$

8. $50 \times 83 = 4150$, $47 \times 83 = 3901$
9. $100 \times 41 = 4100$, $99 \times 41 = 4059$
10. $50 \times 79 = 3950$, $51 \times 79 = 4029$
11. $100 \times 37 = 3700$, $103 \times 37 = 3811$
12. $50 \times 76 = 3800$, $53 \times 76 = 4028$
13. Petra, Joshua, Karim

PCM 53
Coordinates

1. (2, 3)
2. (5, 2)
3. (2, ⁻2)
4. (⁻2, 1)
5. (3, ⁻5)
6. (⁻3, ⁻2)
7. (⁻4, 4)
8. (0, 3)
9. (⁻4, ⁻4)
10. (0, ⁻3)
11. (⁻4, 0)
12. (1, 0)

PCM 54
Coordinate game

No answers required.

PCM 55
Octahedron

No answers required.

PCM 56
Rooftop puzzle

No answers required.

Block C2
PCM 57
Tennis courts

1. 264
2. 132

3. 192
4. 36
5. 104
6. 44
7. 160
8. 140
9. 176

PCM 58
Cubes

Cube	Number of cubes	Surface area
$1 \times 1 \times 1$	1	6 cm²
$2 \times 2 \times 2$	8	24 cm²
$3 \times 3 \times 3$	27	54 cm²
$4 \times 4 \times 4$	64	96 cm²
$5 \times 5 \times 5$	125	150 cm²
$6 \times 6 \times 6$	216	216 cm²
$10 \times 10 \times 10$	1000	600 cm²

Answers about the patterns may vary.
A possible answer is:
surface area = number of cubes
× (6 ÷ length).

PCM 59
Area of triangles

1. 10 cm²
2. 9 cm²
3. 13·5 cm²
4. 4·5 cm²
5. 37·5 cm²
6. 21 cm²
7. 27·5 cm²

PCM 60
Mean averages

1. 6
2. 8
3. 14

4. 22
5. 5
6. 11
7. 10
8. 9
9. 50
10. 28
11. 5
12. 7·5
13. 4
14. 13·25
15. 5·75
16. 5·25
17. 9·5
18. 10

PCM 61
Dice averages

Answers will vary.

PCM 62
Fahrenheit and Centigrade

1. 50°F
2. 104°F
3. 122°F
4. 59°F
5. 32°F
6. 77°F
7. 21°C
8. 49°C
9. 26·5°C
10. 10°C
11. 37·5°C
12. 24°C
13. 18·5°C
14. 40·5°C

PCM 63
Inches and centimetres

Answers will vary.

Block D2

PCM 64
Addition pyramids

1.
```
            3·1
        1·6     1·5
     0·9    0·7    0·8
  0·3   0·6   0·1   0·7
```

2.
```
            8·8
        4·9     3·9
     2·7    2·2    1·7
  1·4   1·3   0·9   0·8
```

3.
```
            3·56
        1·73    1·83
     0·74   0·99   0·84
  0·21  0·53  0·46  0·38
```

4.
```
            4·06
        2·04    2·02
     1·13   0·91   1·11
  0·93   0·2   0·71   0·4
```

5.
```
               25·31
          15·26    10·05
       9·17    6·09    3·96
     5·4   3·77   2·32   1·64
  3·25  2·15  1·62   0·7   0·94
```

PCM 65
Difference pyramids

1.
```
             0
         0·1    0·1
      0·6    0·5    0·4
   0·9   0·3   0·8   0·4
```

2.

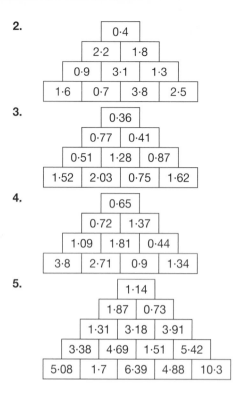

3.

4.

5.

3.	25
4.	9
5.	100
6.	36
7.	49
8.	64
9.	100
10.	36
11.	81
12.	49
13.	121
14.	144
15.	196
16.	289
17.	361
18.	441
19.	400
20.	324
21.	169
22.	576

PCM 66
Addition game
Answers will vary.

PCM 67
Adding
1. 3675
2. 3419
3. 4730
4. 8065
5. 8567
6. 12 219
7. 8918
8. 12 187
9. 6744

PCM 68
Square numbers
1. 9
2. 25

PCM 69
Square numbers

Number	Estimated square	Calculated square	Difference
13		169	
21		441	
37		1369	
63		3969	
28		784	
92		8464	
2·4		5·76	
1·9		3·61	
3·5		12·25	
7·4		54·76	

Answers for estimates and differences will vary.

PCM 70
Triangle patterns

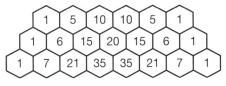

Answers about the patterns will vary.
Possible answers include:
triangular numbers 1, 3, 6, 10, 15 and 21
appear in a diagonal line starting from the
third row;
numbers 1–7 appear in a diagonal line
starting from the second row.

PCM 71
Sequences

1. 65, 76, 87, 98
2. 108, 117, 126, 135
3. 16, 32, 64, 128
4. 128, 109, 90, 71
5. 21, 28, 36
6. 36, 49, 64, 81
7. 85, 102, 119, 136
8. ⁻3, ⁻7, ⁻11, ⁻15, ⁻19
9. 13, 21
10. 3·25, 3·5, 3·75, 4, 4·25
11. 3·3, 4·2, 5·1, 6, 6·9
12. 4·7, 5, 5·3, 5·6, 5·9

Block E2
PCM 72
Multiplying game

Answers will vary.

PCM 73
Multiplying

Answers will vary.

PCM 74
Multiplying

1. £8
2. £16
3. £32
4. £24
5. £9
6. £45
7. £27
8. £63
9. £35
10. £245
11. £105
12. £315
13. £30
14. £150
15. £90
16. £180
17. £40
18. £80
19. £280
20. £200

PCM 75
Multiplying

x	400	80	2000	600	800	1200
$\frac{3}{10}$	120	24	600	180	240	360
$\frac{2}{5}$	160	32	800	240	320	480
$\frac{7}{100}$	28	5·6	140	42	56	84
$\frac{9}{20}$	180	36	900	270	360	540
$\frac{7}{10}$	280	56	1400	420	560	840
$\frac{3}{4}$	300	60	1500	450	600	900
$\frac{4}{5}$	320	64	1600	480	640	960
$\frac{11}{20}$	220	44	1100	330	440	660
$\frac{51}{100}$	204	40·8	1020	306	408	612
$\frac{19}{20}$	380	76	1900	570	760	1140

PCM 76
Fractions and decimals

1. Answer provided
2. 0·09
3. 1·7
4. 3·11
5. 2·09
6. 0·854
7. 6·127
8. 8·083
9. 1·5
10. 3·19
11. 0·4
12. 0·4
13. 7·25
14. 3·75
15. 8·8
16. 0·55
17. 1·45
18. 0·74
19. 0·84
20. 1·28

PCM 77
Fractions and decimals

1. $\frac{3}{5} = 0\cdot6$ or $\frac{3}{6} = 0\cdot5$
2. $\frac{8}{5} = 1\cdot6$
3. $\frac{9}{10} = 0\cdot9$
4. $\frac{9}{2} = 4\cdot5$
5. $\frac{13}{5} = 2\cdot6$ or $\frac{13}{2} = 6\cdot5$
6. $\frac{14}{10} = 1\cdot4$
7. $\frac{31}{5} = 6\cdot2$
8. $\frac{8}{20} = 0\cdot4$
9. $\frac{14}{20} = 0\cdot7$
10. $\frac{60}{40} = 1\cdot5$

PCM 78
Divisibility

1. 3, 6
2. 3, 9
3. 3, 6, 9
4. 3
5. 3, 6
6. 3, 6
7. 3
8. 3, 6
9. 3, 9
10. 2, 4, 8
11. 2, 4, 8
12. 2, 4
13. 2, 4, 8
14. 2
15. 2, 4
16. 2
17. 2, 4
18. 2, 4, 8

PCM 79
Divisibility

Answers may vary. Possible answers include:
18, 27, 16, 45, 48, 32, 63, 90, 50
42, 93, 12, 75, 36, 48, 81, 60, 50

Block A3
PCM 80
Positive and negative numbers

1. 5
2. 10
3. 5
4. 4
5. 10
6. 8
7. 9
8. 16
9. 18
10. 5
11. 6
12. 8
13. 9
14. 27

15. 20
16. 21
17. 59
18. 19
19. 98
20. 61

PCM 81

Positive and negative numbers

d	3	⁻2	4	⁻5
⁻7	10	5	11	2
6	3	8	2	11
10	7	12	6	15
⁻9	12	7	13	4

d	27	⁻13	⁻18	9
⁻11	38	2	7	20
14	13	27	32	5
23	4	36	41	14
⁻16	43	3	2	25

d	0·3	⁻0·7	⁻0·5	1·1
⁻2·7	3	2	2·2	3·8
⁻3·6	3·9	2·9	3·1	4·7
⁻3·5	3·8	2·8	3	4·6
⁻1·2	1·5	0·5	0·7	2·3

d	⁻5·3	6·2	⁻7·4	1·9
2·8	8·1	3·4	10·2	0·9
⁻3·7	1·6	9·9	3·7	5·6
4·5	9·8	1·7	11·9	2·6
⁻1·6	3·7	7·8	5·8	3·5

PCM 82

Fractions as percentages

1. 30
2. 90
3. 11
4. 25
5. 50
6. 35
7. 60
8. 75
9. 74
10. 20
11. 5
12. 10
13. 2
14. 80
15. 26
16. 4
17. 95
18. 35
19. 98
20. 36

PCM 83

Percentages

1. £8
2. £4
3. £60
4. £40
5. £25
6. £12
7. £11
8. £15
9. £6
10. £6
11. £30
12. £24
13. £30
14. £6·30
15. £32
16. £36
17. £0·80
18. £1·80
19. £3
20. £1·20

PCM 84
Percentages

1. Answer provided.
2. $33\cdot3\% = \frac{1}{3}$
   $\frac{1}{3}$ of £96 = £32
   $33\cdot3\%$ of £96 = £32
3. $75\% = \frac{3}{4}$
   $\frac{1}{4}$ of £124 = £31
   $\frac{3}{4}$ of £124 = £93
   75% of £124 = £93
4. $20\% = \frac{1}{5}$
   $\frac{1}{5}$ of £45 = £9
   20% of £45 = £9
5. $25\% = \frac{1}{4}$
   $\frac{1}{2}$ of £480 = £240
   $\frac{1}{4}$ of £480 = £120
   25% of £480 = £120
6. $75\% = \frac{3}{4}$
   $\frac{1}{4}$ of £720 = £180
   $\frac{3}{4}$ of £720 = £540
7. $10\% = \frac{1}{10}$
   $\frac{1}{10}$ of £66 = £6.60
   10% of £66 = £6.60
8. $33\cdot3\% = \frac{1}{3}$
   $\frac{1}{3}$ of £135 = £45
   $33\cdot3\%$ of £135 = £45
9. $50\% = \frac{1}{2}$
   $\frac{1}{2}$ of £91.50 = £45.75
   50% of £91.50 = £45.75
10. Answer provided.
11. $25\% = \frac{1}{4}$
    $\frac{1}{4}$ of £10.60 = £2.65
    New price:
    £10.60 – £2.65 = £7.95
12. $\frac{1}{4}$ of £20.10 = £5.025
    £20.10 – £5.025 = £15.075 → £15.08
13. $\frac{1}{4}$ of £14.36 = £3.59
    £14.36 – £3.59 = £10.77

PCM 85
Multiplying

1. 3264
2. 4482
3. 9792
4. 6672
5. 12 236
6. 19 158
7. 7533
8. 13 824
9. 32 144

PCM 86
Multiplying

Answers will vary.

PCM 87
Multiplying

1. 6
   $2\cdot4$
   $8\cdot4$
2. 12
   $1\cdot6$
   $13\cdot6$
3. 30
   $3\cdot5$
   $33\cdot5$
4. 16
   $1\cdot4$
   $0\cdot02$
   $17\cdot42$
5. 24
   $1\cdot2$
   $0\cdot18$
   $25\cdot38$
6. 15
   $0\cdot3$
   $0\cdot18$
   $15\cdot48$

7. $5 \times 4 = 20$
$5 \times 0\cdot2 = 1$
$5 \times 0\cdot06 = 0\cdot3$
$5 \times 4\cdot26 = 21\cdot3$

8. $4 \times 3 = 12$
$4 \times 0\cdot7 = 2\cdot8$
$4 \times 0\cdot07 = 0\cdot28$
$4 \times 3\cdot77 = 15\cdot08$

9. $3 \times 8 = 24$
$3 \times 0\cdot6 = 1\cdot8$
$3 \times 0\cdot04 = 0\cdot12$
$3 \times 8\cdot64 = 25\cdot92$

Block B3

PCM 88
Adding decimals

1. 6·37
2. 12·79
3. 14·65
4. 6·45
5. 10·10
6. 13·82
7. 17·91
8. 6·40
9. 9·03
10. 17·29
11. 21·03
12. 10·54

PCM 89
Addition game

Answers will vary.

PCM 90
Subtraction game

Answers will vary.

PCM 91
Subtracting 4-digit numbers

1. 2212
2. 2529
3. 3315
4. 6476
5. 7149
6. 1129
7. 3733
8. 4265
9. 2557
10. 3274
11. 3223
12. 3454

PCM 92
Subtracting decimals

1. 2·13
2. 4·47
3. 3·33
4. 5·35
5. 5·25
6. 3·44
7. 2·31
8. 2·83
9. 1·38
10. 1·09
11. 1·65
12. 2·13

PCM 93
Subtraction game

Answers will vary.

PCM 94
Litres, millilitres, gallons, pints

1. >
2. =
3. <
4. <
5. >

6. >
7. >
8. >
9. >
10. >
11. >
12. <
13. <
14. =
15. >
16. <
17. <
18. <

Block C3

PCM 95
Probability

Answers will vary.

PCM 96
Dice probabilities

1. $\frac{1}{6}$
2. $\frac{1}{6}$
3. $\frac{3}{6}$ or $\frac{1}{2}$
4. $\frac{3}{6}$ or $\frac{1}{2}$
5. $\frac{4}{6}$ or $\frac{2}{3}$
6. $\frac{2}{6}$ or $\frac{1}{3}$
7. $\frac{2}{6}$ or $\frac{1}{3}$
8. $\frac{2}{6}$ or $\frac{1}{3}$
9. $\frac{2}{6}$ or $\frac{1}{3}$
10. $\frac{4}{6}$ or $\frac{2}{3}$
11. $\frac{4}{6}$ or $\frac{2}{3}$
12. $\frac{4}{6}$ or $\frac{2}{3}$
13. $\frac{2}{6}$ or $\frac{1}{3}$
14. $\frac{1}{6}$
15. $\frac{3}{6}$ or $\frac{1}{2}$
16. $\frac{5}{6}$
17. $\frac{4}{6}$ or $\frac{2}{3}$
18. $\frac{2}{6}$ or $\frac{1}{3}$

PCM 97
Pie charts

1. adventure
2. soaps
3. 6
4. 8
5. 2
6. 3
7. 5
8. 3
9. $\frac{5}{16}$
10. $\frac{6}{16}$ or $\frac{3}{8}$
11. $\frac{2}{16}$ or $\frac{1}{8}$
12. $\frac{3}{16}$
13. $\frac{3}{16}$
14. $\frac{8}{16}$ or $\frac{1}{2}$

PCM 98
Pie charts

Answers will vary.

PCM 99
Perimeter

1. 520 cm
2. 420 cm
3. 304 cm
4. 330 cm
5. 112 cm
6. 258 cm
7. 136 cm
8. 260 cm
9. 300 cm

PCM 100
Perimeter

1. 3·4
   3·9
   6·5
   7·4
   8·4
   16·2
   P = 45·8 cm

2. 5·2
5·8
5·9
6·2
10·0
P = 33·1 cm
3. 4·2
8·6
8·7
10·0
P = 31·5 cm

PCM 101
Days

1. 34 days
2. 37 days
3. 18 days
4. 45 days
5. 45 days
6. 16 days
7. 61 days
8. 93 days
9. 113 days

Block D3
PCM 102
Reflecting points

1. (2, ⁻3)
2. (3, 3)
3. (3, 0)
4. (⁻3, 0)
5. (⁻2, 2)
6. (0, 4)
7. (⁻4, ⁻1)
8. (2, 4)
9. (⁻2, ⁻4)
10. (5, ⁻5)
11. (2, 4)
12. (2, ⁻2)
13. (3, 0)
14. (⁻5, 1)
15. (⁻2, ⁻4)
16. (4, 1)

17. (⁻3, ⁻3)
18. (⁻2, 3)

PCM 103
Reflecting shapes

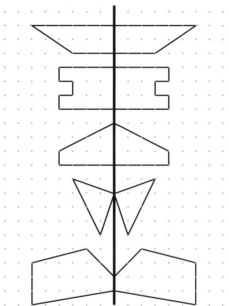

PCM 104
Translating points

1. (1, 1)
2. (⁻2, ⁻2)
3. (2, ⁻4)
4. (⁻3, 3)
5. (1, 4)
6. (1, 4)
7. (3, ⁻1)
8. (⁻5, 2)
9. (6, ⁻2)
10. (⁻7, ⁻3)

PCM 105
Rotating shapes

1. (3, 2)
2. (⁻3, 4)

3. (3, ⁻2)
4. (1, 0)
5. (5, 0)
6. (5, 0)
7. (⁻1, 6)
8. (7, 2)
9. (3, ⁻2)
10. (7, 2)

PCM 106

Dividing

1.
```
      154
  3)462
  - 300      100 × 3
    162
  - 150       50 × 3
     12
  -  12        4 × 3
```

2.
```
      134
  4)536
  - 400      100 × 4
    136
  - 120       30 × 4
     16
  -  16        4 × 4
```

3.
```
      128 r3
  5)643
  - 500      100 × 5
    143
  - 100       20 × 5
     43
  -  40        8 × 5
      3
```

4.
```
      180 r3
  4)723
  - 400      100 × 4
    323
  - 320       80 × 4
      3
```

5.
```
      183
  3)549
  - 300      100 × 3
    249
  - 240       80 × 3
      9
  -   9        3 × 3
```

6.
```
      139 r2
  6)836
  - 600      100 × 6
    236
  - 180       30 × 6
     56
  -  54        9 × 6
      2
```

7.
```
      175
  5)875
  - 500      100 × 5
    375
  - 350       70 × 5
     25
  -  25        5 × 5
```

8.
```
      131 r6
  7)923
  - 700      100 × 7
    223
  - 210       30 × 7
     13
  -   7        1 × 7
      6
```

9.
```
      117
  8)936
  - 800      100 × 8
    136
  -  80       10 × 8
     56
  -  56        7 × 8
```

PCM 107

Dividing

Answers will vary.

PCM 108
Dividing decimals

1.
```
      6·4
   2)12·8
   - 12      6  × 2
     0·8
   - 0·8     0·4 × 2
```

2.
```
     11·7
   3)35·1
   - 30      10  × 3
     5·1
   -  3       1  × 3
     2·1
   - 2·1     0·7 × 3
```

3.
```
     21·6
   4)86·4
   - 80      20  × 4
     6·4
   -  4       1  × 4
     2·4
   - 2·4     0·6 × 4
```

4.
```
     13·5
   5)67·5
   - 50      10  × 5
    17·5
   - 15       3  × 5
     2·5
   - 2·5     0·5 × 5
```

5.
```
     24·2
   4)96·8
   - 80      20  × 4
    16·8
   - 16       4  × 4
     0·8
   - 0·8     0·2 × 4
```

6.
```
     24·2
   3)72·6
   - 60      20  × 3
    12·6
   - 12       4  × 3
     0·6
   - 0·6     0·2 × 3
```

7.
```
     13·1
   6)78·6
   - 60      10  × 6
    18·6
   - 18       3  × 6
     0·6
   - 0·6     0·1 × 6
```

8.
```
     18·5
   5)92·5
   - 50      10  × 5
    42·5
   - 40       8  × 5
     2·5
   - 2·5     0·5 × 5
```

9.
```
     11·7
   8)93·6
   - 80      10  × 8
    13·6
   -  8       1  × 8
     5·6
   - 5·6     0·7 × 8
```

Block E3
PCM 109
Proportion

1. $\frac{3}{4}$
$\frac{1}{4}$

2. $\frac{2}{5}$
$\frac{3}{5}$

3. $\frac{3}{8}$
$\frac{5}{8}$

4. $\frac{3}{5}$
$\frac{2}{5}$

5. $\frac{7}{12}$
$\frac{5}{12}$

6. $\frac{1}{2}$
$\frac{1}{2}$

7. $\frac{10}{21}$
$\frac{11}{21}$

8. $\frac{5}{6}$
$\frac{1}{6}$

9. $\frac{7}{10}$
$\frac{3}{10}$

PCM 110

Proportion

1. 4 blue, 2 red, 1 yellow
2. 5 blue, 2 red, 1 yellow
3. 4 blue, 3 red
4. 6 blue, 8 red, 4 yellow, 4 green
5. 2 blue, 8 red, 5 yellow, 2 green
6. 6 blue, 12 red, 8 yellow, 4 green
7. 6 blue, 9 red, 12 yellow, 3 green
8. 7 blue, 7 red, 8 yellow
9. 12 blue, 9 red, 6 yellow, 8 green

PCM 111

Ratio

1. 20:5 or 4:1
2. 5:15 or 1:3
3. 15:6 or 5:2
4. 6:30 or 1:5
5. 6:5
6. 15:20 or 3:4
7. 20:6 or 10:3
8. 5:30 or 1:6
9. 30:15 or 2:1
10. 30:20 or 3:2
11. 5:60 or 1:12
12. 15:60 or 1:4
13. 20:60 or 1:3
14. 6:60 or 1:10

PCM 112

Ratio

1. 2 squares shaded
2. 8 squares shaded
3. 4 squares shaded
4. 4 squares shaded
5. 5 squares shaded
6. 6 squares shaded
7. 3 squares shaded
8. 5 squares shaded
9. 6 squares shaded
10. 15 squares shaded
11. 10 squares shaded
12. 1 square shaded

PCM 113

Prime numbers

1. 7, 11
2. 13, 17
3. 7, 11
4. 19, 23
5. 31, 37
6. 17, 19
7. 41, 43
8. 53, 59
9. 37, 41
10. 61, 67
11. 97, 101
12. 73, 79
13. 79, 83
14. 83, 89
15. 43, 47
16. 89, 97

PCM 114

Prime numbers

Answers will vary.

PCM 115

Prime factors

1.

2	42
3	21
7	7
	1

2.

2	38
19	19
	1

3.

3	75
5	25
5	5
	1

4.

2	24
2	12
2	6
3	3
	1

5.

2	124
2	62
31	31
	1

6.

2	136
2	68
2	34
17	17
	1

7.

2	98
7	49
7	7
	1

8.

5	125
5	25
5	5
	1

9.

2	104
2	52
2	26
13	13
	1

10.

2	102
3	51
17	17
	1

11.

2	88
2	44
2	22
11	11
	1

12.

2	212
2	106
53	53
	1